# Design and Con

# of Tube Guitar Amplifiers



*Third Edition*

**Robert Megantz**

Printed in the United States of America.

TacTec is a sole proprietorship registered in San Jose, CA, USA.



Web Site: www.translucidamps.com

E-mail: bob@tactec.biz

ISBN 978-0-615-29180-2

# Contents

# Preface

All musicians agree that beautiful tone is essential to a satisfying musical performance. The electric guitar is unique in that its tone depends not only on the instrument but also on the amplifier used. You can argue that the sound of other amplified instruments, such as the bass guitar and electric piano, also depends on the amplification used, but in most cases a high-power, low-distortion, wide-bandwidth system with equalization is optimal for these applications. The guitar requires much more signal processing, including distortion, reverberation, tremolo, and other effects.

In fact, you should think of the amplifier as part of the instrument. Because a guitar amplifier is as much a musical instrument as an electronic apparatus, it must be conceived and designed as much from a musical as from a technical perspective. You must ignore some of the classic rules regarding audio design. For example, designing amplifier stages for the lowest possible distortion is no longer required or desired. Other rules remain applicable. For example, proper grounding and shielding is needed to prevent excessive hum and noise. Choosing the appropriate design criteria is based on both aesthetics, the realm of the artist, and technical issues, the realm of the engineer.

To make matters even murkier, the aesthetics are subjective. That is, each musician has his or her own idea of what tone is desired, which is affected by the type of music being played. Jazz players want a fat tone with rolled-off highs. Rock players want a more distorted tone. Country players want a cleaner, twangier sound. Two or more different tones are often required, the most common being a "clean" tone for rhythm and a "dirty" tone for leads.

Furthermore, the languages of music and engineering are different, making effective communication between musicians and amplifier designers difficult. Musicians often have little technical knowledge, and engineers find it difficult to apply a musical aesthetic to their design efforts. Some of the most successful amplifier designs have been collaborations between musicians and engineers, where the musician "tunes" the design by explaining his or her desires in musical terms, and the engineer then translates those desires to amplifier design parameters and makes the required design changes.

Many musicians find tube-based designs to be the best-sounding. Tube amplifier designs have been embraced for their overload characteristics, touch sensitivity, and general musicality. Most tube amps are quite simple, and the technical concepts can be easily grasped if you have a basic understanding of scientific principles and high school-level algebra.

*Design and Construction of Tube Guitar Amplifiers* was written for musicians and hobbyists new to the subject, so I have simplified the discussion of some topics to a level that can be easily understood by the target audience. To audio engineers and other more experienced readers I offer my apologies in advance. You can find more detailed and advanced information in the references listed in the Bibliography, as well as in many standard engineering textbooks.

*Design and Construction of Tube Guitar Amplifiers* provides an easy-to-understand yet comprehensive overview of all aspects of tube amplifier design. Reading this book will allow you to fully understand why your amplifier sounds like it does. In addition you will learn how to design, construct, maintain, repair, and modify amps, and the real meaning of design concepts such as bias and class of operation.

— Chapter 1 introduces the scientific principles used in audio design. If you're new to the subject, you should study Chapter 1 carefully, as you must understand these basic electronic engineering concepts to follow the rest of the book.

— Chapter 2 describes the basic building blocks of an amplifier, and describes how to design the various stages.

— Chapter 3 describes overdrive, reverberation, and tremolo, three effects that are commonly found in tube amplifiers, and how to design an effects loop, which is used to incorporate external effects.

— Chapter 4 explains how to build and troubleshoot tube amplifiers.

Additional information on where you can buy components and design data for various tubes is included in the appendices.

I hope you enjoy the book, and that you finish it with an increased understanding of how to design and build tube guitar amplifiers.

Bob Megantz
April 2009
San Jose, CA

*Design and Construction of Tube Guitar Amplifiers* has proven to be popular, necessitating a second printing. Several readers have suggested changes, for which I am grateful. In addition, a few errors in the first printing have been corrected. Overall, the book has stood the test of time, and I am looking forward to continuing my efforts to increase your understanding and improve your use of tube guitar amplifiers.

Bob Megantz
July 2011
San Jose, CA

# Acknowledgements

I’d like to thank everyone who helped me in my musical and electronic endeavors throughout the years. Special thanks go to:

Ken Leyva, who prepared all of the graphics, David Espinosa, who assisted in editing the manuscript and provided much of the reference material, Ron Morton, who produced the book, and Earles McCaul and Tom Cantrell, whose helpful criticisms of the first printing led to many of the corrections and additions in the second printing.

I’d also like to thank my parents, who bought me my first electric guitar and my first tube electronic project, a Heathkit shortwave radio.

Photo in Figure 4.15 courtesy of Mark Huss.

Tube characteristic charts in Figures B.3, B.4, B.10, and B.14 courtesy of Audiomatica Srl.

# Chapter 1
# Electronic Fundamentals

To fully understand guitar amplifier design, you must first understand the language and concepts used by audio engineers. Like musicians, engineers use a particular vocabulary and set of rules in their work, which allows them to effectively communicate with others and understand technical materials such as component specifications, test procedures and data.

Readers with a technical background can skim the material in this chapter and refer back when necessary. If this information is new to you, please carefully read and fully understand this chapter before moving on.

## Current and Voltage

Current is defined as a flow of electrons, measured in units of *amperes* (abbreviated *A*). Electrons are negatively-charged subatomic particles that can be generated in a number of ways, as we will see later. Electrical current is analogous to the amount of water flowing in a pipe, which depends on the size of the pipe, the pressure, and the amount of water available.

Voltage is the electrical potential between two points of a circuit, expressed in *volts* (abbreviated *V*, or sometimes *B*). Potential means the potential energy of an electric field to cause a current to flow in a conductor. Higher voltages have higher potential energy, and thus cause higher currents to flow, all other things remaining equal. Voltage is analogous to pressure in a hydraulic system.

Since electrons are negatively charged, they are repelled by a negative voltage and attracted by a positive voltage, and thus flow from negative to positive. However, it is useful to define *conventional* current as flowing from positive to negative, and that is the convention we use in this book. Conventional current is just the opposite (negative) of electron current.

*Direct* current (abbreviated *DC*) is current that flows in one direction only. DC is induced by voltage of constant polarity, either positive or negative. DC voltages are produced by batteries and the power supplies we will study later in this book.

*Alternating* current (abbreviated *AC*) is current whose direction of flow varies. AC is induced by a voltage of varying polarity. The most common example is the voltage supplied to your house by your power company, but there are many other examples, including the output voltage of a guitar pickup and the voltages present at the speaker terminals of an amplifier.

As we will see later, a wide range of AC and DC voltages are present in guitar amplifiers.

A *voltage source* keeps voltage constant but allows current to vary. Examples of voltage sources include batteries and the power supplies described in Chapter 2.

A *current source* keeps current constant but allows voltage to vary. We can implement a current source in several ways, as we discuss later.

## Power

Power (measured in *watts*, abbreviated *W*) is the product of voltage and current:

$$W = V \times I \quad \textbf{Equation 1.1}$$

Power is generated by both AC and DC. You need to calculate power when designing the power supply and output stage of an amplifier, and when specifying components used in the amplifier.

## Frequency

Frequency is the number of times a signal repeats in one second. The unit of frequency is *Hertz* (abbreviated *Hz*). Figure 1.1 shows two AC signals, each of which consists of positive and negative halves. The upper wave (a) completes one cycle in 1 second, so its frequency is 1Hz. The lower wave (b) completes two cycles in one second, so its frequency is 2Hz.

Both waves shown in Figure 1.1 are called *sine* waves, and are commonly used as test signals because they consist of a single frequency. All other waves, including those produced by guitars and other musical instruments, are more complex, consisting of the lowest *fundamental* frequency and higher frequency *harmonics*.

**Figure 1.1** Measurement of Frequency

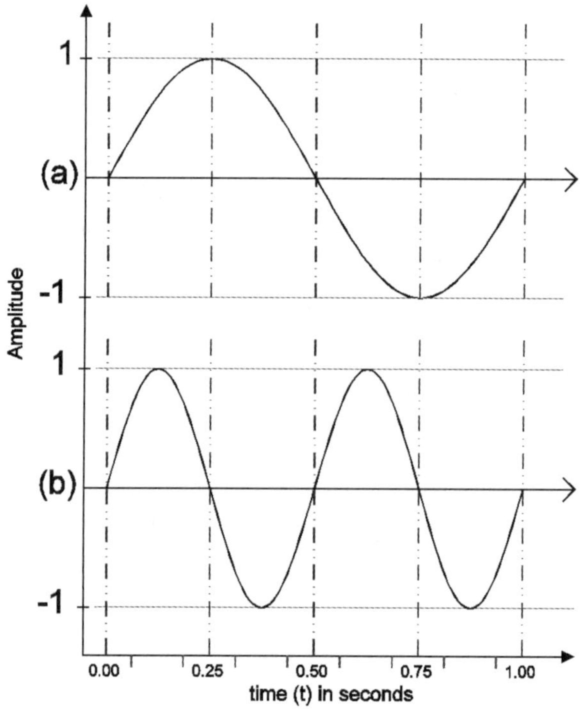

## Phase

You can also delineate a wave in *degrees*. One full cycle corresponds to 360 degrees, so each half cycle constitutes 180 degrees, each quarter cycle 90 degrees, and so on. The time associated with each degree depends on the frequency of the wave.

Phase (in degrees) describes the relative position of two waves of the same frequency. In Figure 1.2, you can see that the wave shown in a) begins rising positively at 0 and 360 degrees, while the wave shown in b) begins rising positively at 90 and 450 degrees. Thus, wave b) is 90 degrees out of phase with wave a). Wave b) is said to *lag* wave a) by 90 degrees, and wave a) is said to *lead* wave b) by 90 degrees. Wave c) lags wave a) by 180 degrees and wave b) by 90 degrees. Waves a) and c) are said to be *out of phase*, and, if added together, cancel. On the other hand, adding two waves that are *in phase* results in a wave with greater amplitude than either.

**Figure 1.2** Relative Phase

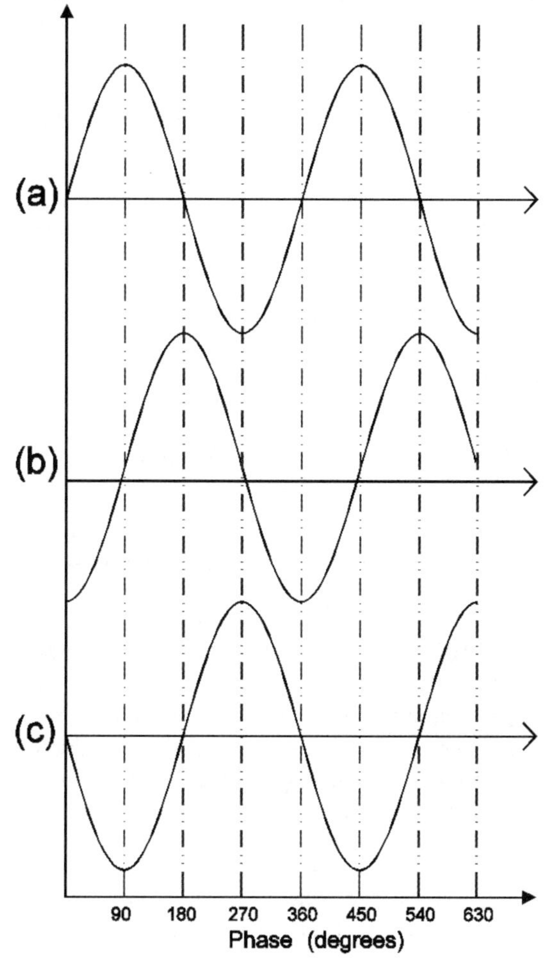


For the wave shown in Figure 1.1 a), zero seconds corresponds to zero degrees, 0.25 seconds corresponds to 90 degrees, 0.5 seconds corresponds to 180 degrees, 0.75 seconds corresponds to 270 degrees, and one second corresponds to 360 degrees. You can see that the sine wave has an amplitude of 0 at 0, 180, and 360 degrees, an amplitude of 1 at 90 degrees, and an amplitude of -1 at 270 degrees. For the 2Hz wave in Figure 1.1 b), 0 seconds corresponds to 0 degrees, but 0.25 seconds corresponds to 180 degrees and 0.5 seconds corresponds to 360 degrees, as the wave completes one full cycle in 0.5 seconds.

Guitar *feedback* results when the acoustic wave coming from the amplifier is in phase with the wave generated by the guitar string and body, and the two waves sum to create a wave loud enough to excite the strings and sustain the tone. The guitar must be the proper distance from the amplifier for the two waves to add in phase, and, as waves in the air of different frequency have different wavelengths, the proper distance depends on which note is being played.

*Negative* feedback, where an out-of-phase signal is intentionally added to a signal, is also used in guitar amplifiers, as we discuss in Chapter 2 in the section on output stages.

## Decibels

The human auditory system responds to sound in an exponential manner in both amplitude and frequency. If, for example, you listen to a sine wave whose amplitude is 1V and then increase its level to 2V, you hear an increase in volume. If you then raise the 2V signal by an additional 1V to 3V, you also hear an increase in volume, but the increase is less than the increase noticed when changing from 1V to 2V. In fact, you have to raise the level to around 4V to note the same increase in volume.

Furthermore, the range of levels perceptible by the human hearing system is very large, on the order of 1,000,000,000,000 to one, and numbers that range this widely are difficult to work with without some kind of mathematical system to simplify matters.

For these reasons we use the *decibel* scale (abbreviated *dB*) to denote relative levels. It is based on logarithms, which are exponential powers, in this case, of 10. The formula for determining the difference between two voltages in dB is:

$$dB = 20 \times \log_{10} \frac{V_2}{V_1}.$$ **Equation 1.2**

For example, if $V_2 = 10V$ and $V_1 = 1V$, $\log \frac{V_2}{V_1} = 1$ and the difference between the two voltages is 20dB. If $V_2 = 100V$ and $V_1 = 1V$, the difference in dB is 40 (20 x 2). So, the difference in dB between 1V and 10V is the same as the difference in dB between 10V and 100V (40dB – 20dB = 20dB). Using the dB scale allows us to linearize the inherently exponential nature of signals in amplifier circuits, which, as we will learn later, makes circuit design and analysis more convenient. Among other things, we can add and subtract decibels, and they can be negative (if $V_2$ is less than $V_1$) or positive (as in the example above). You can compute logarithms easily using a scientific calculator.

It is important to emphasize that a number in dB only represents the relative level difference between two voltages. Unless one of the voltages is known, the absolute level is unknown. Several reference levels can be used, such as *dBV* (voltage relative to $1V_{rms}$) and *dBu* (voltage relative to $0.775V_{rms}$). *Root-mean-square (rms)* is one way to measure the amplitude of a signal, and is described, along with other methods, in the section on AC Signal Amplitude later in this chapter. The reference level must be defined and explicitly stated. Saying "this signal has a level of 60dB" tells us nothing about its absolute level.

## Octaves

The situation is similar with respect to frequency. If you listen to a 100Hz tone and then increase the tone's frequency by 100Hz to 200Hz, the new tone is one octave higher. If you increase the 200Hz tone by an additional 100Hz, the 300Hz tone is not one octave higher than the 200Hz tone. In fact, you must double the frequency to raise the tone one octave, so you must raise the 200Hz tone to 400Hz, and you must raise a 400Hz tone to 800Hz. Since the range of human hearing extends from 20Hz to 20,000Hz, the lowest octave spans 20Hz (from 20Hz to 40Hz), while the highest octave spans 10,000Hz (from 10,000Hz to 20,000Hz).

So, for the same reason we use the dB scale for level, we use a logarithmic scale for frequency. The scale is linear by octave, or doubling of frequency (powers of two).

## Metric Prefixes

Another way to more easily handle very large or small numbers is to use the system of metric prefixes. The prefixes commonly used in electronics are listed in Table 1.1.

**Table 1.1** Metric Prefixes

| Prefix | Multiplier |
|---|---|
| Mega (M) | 1,000,000 |
| Kilo (k) | 1,000 |
| - | 1 |
| Milli (m) | .001 |
| Micro (u) | .000001 |
| Nano (n) | .000000001 |
| Pico (p) | .000000000001 |

So, for example, you can express 20,000Hz as 20kHz. Note that each prefix listed covers a range of values of 1,000. We use metric prefixes extensively throughout this text.

## Resistance and Ohm's Law

Resistance is the degree to which a material opposes the flow of current. It is a fundamental physical property. For example, copper, silver, and gold have very low resistance; they are called *conductors.* Glass, ceramics, plastics and rubber, on the other hand, have high resistance, and are called *insulators*. Other materials, such as carbon and wires or films made of various metal alloys, have moderate resistance and can be used in *resistors,* devices that provide a constant, known resistance.

Resistance is measured in *Ohms* (abbreviated Ω). It is more precisely defined by Ohm's Law, which states:

$$V = I \times R$$ **Equation 1.3**,

where V is in volts, I is in amperes, and R is in ohms.

In Figure 1.3, resistor R has current I flowing through it. If R = 20Ω and I = 2A, then V, using Ohm's Law, is 20 x 2 = 40V. Note the schematic symbol for a resistor used in Figure 1.3.

**Figure 1.3** Ohm's Law

By moving terms around, we can rewrite Ohm's Law as:

$I = \frac{V}{R}$ **Equation 1.4**, or $R = \frac{V}{I}$. **Equation 1.5**

Again referring to Figure 1.3, if V = 50V and R = 100Ω, then the current I is $\frac{50}{100}$ = 0.5A. If we apply 500V across R and measure a current of 0.1A flowing through R, then the value of R is $\frac{500}{0.1}$ = 5,000Ω, or 5kΩ.

## Impedance

*Impedance* (abbreviated *Z*) is a more complex type of resistance, where the resistance and phase between the input and output signals change with frequency. Impedance, like resistance, is measured in ohms.

Resistors exhibit no change in resistance over frequency, and produce no phase shifts in signals, so their impedance is equal to their resistance.

*Capacitors* and *inductors*, discussed in the following two sections, exhibit more complex, frequency-dependent behavior.

## Capacitance

Capacitance is the amount of electric charge that can be stored for a given electric potential. You can visualize this concept by imagining two parallel sheets of metal held apart a fixed distance. If we apply a voltage across the two plates, electrons gather on the negatively-charged plate. If the sheets are larger or closer together, more electrons gather. If certain materials (called *dielectrics)* are placed between the two plates, more electrons gather. The unit of capacitance is the *Farad* (abbreviated *f*).

Later, we will apply this concept to power supplies, since the capacitors in a power supply store charge, which is then supplied to the rest of the amplifier circuit.

Capacitors have another, less obvious property that makes them useful in electronic circuits. When an AC signal is applied, the impedance of a capacitor of value C changes with frequency according to the formula:

$$Z = \frac{1}{2\Pi fC}$$ **Equation 1.6**, where $\Pi = 3.14$.

As you can see from the above equation, the impedance of a capacitor is inversely proportional to both frequency and capacitance. Thus, the impedance of a capacitor decreases as frequency increases, and, at a given frequency, the impedance of a small capacitor is higher than that of a large capacitor. We will explore this concept in the section on voltage dividers, where we show how capacitors can shape frequency response.

Capacitors also affect the phase of signals passing through them. The amount of phase shift depends on frequency. In some cases, these phase shifts are not important, while in others they affect stability or frequency response. In subsequent chapters we will discuss phase considerations in amplifier design.

## Inductance

A current flowing through a coil of wire produces a magnetic field. The magnetic field stores energy, like the electric field in a capacitor. You will find more information on magnetic fields in the Transformer section, later in this chapter.

The ratio of the strength of the field produced to the current flowing is known as the inductance. We measure inductance in *Henrys* (abbreviated *H*). Inductance increases if there are more turns of wire on the coil, or if the coil is wrapped around a ferrous metal.

The impedance of an *inductor* of value L changes with frequency according to the formula:

$$Z = 2\Pi fL\,.$$ **Equation 1.7**

Unlike capacitors, the impedance of an inductor is directly proportional to frequency and inductance. As frequency rises, the impedance of a given inductor rises, and, at a given frequency, the impedance of a larger inductor is greater than that of a smaller inductor. Like capacitors, inductors affect the phase of signals passing through them.

Inductors are used in amplifiers in the power supply, where they are called *chokes*. The power and output transformers, which can be thought of as special types of inductors, are discussed later in this chapter. You can also use inductors in tone control circuits, but we rarely see them used this way in guitar amplifiers because they are expensive and hard to find. One famous application is in the "Cry-Baby" wah-wah pedal, which uses an inductor in its variable filter circuit.

**Figure 1.4** Capacitor and Inductor Schematic Symbols

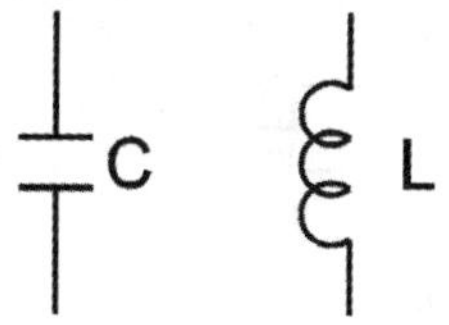


## Voltage and Current Dividing Networks

Resistors, capacitors, and inductors can be configured in many ways to serve different purposes. This section discusses the characteristics of some simple networks.

## *Components in Series*

To calculate the total resistance of two (or more) resistors in series, simply add the values of the individual resistors. Likewise, to calculate the total inductance of two inductors in series, add the values of the individual inductors.

To calculate the total capacitance of two capacitors in series, use inverse addition:

$$\frac{1}{C} = \frac{1}{C_1} + \frac{1}{C_2} \quad \textbf{Equation 1.8}$$

Equation 1.8 is equivalent to:

$$C = \frac{C_1 \times C_2}{C_1 + C_2} \quad \textbf{Equation 1.9}$$

Figure 1.5 shows the formulae for calculating the values of series combinations of resistors, capacitors, and inductors.

**Figure 1.5** Components in Series

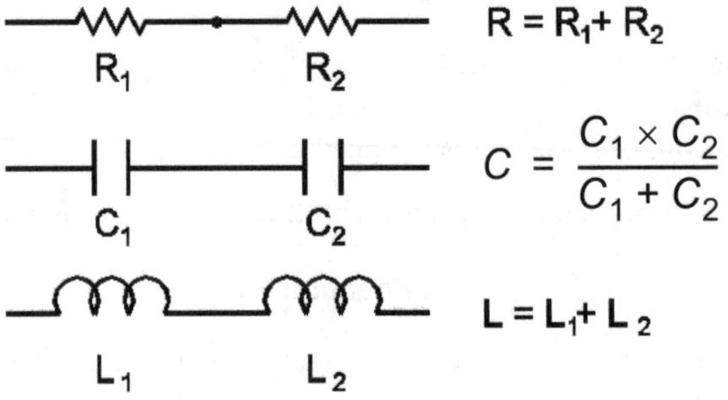


## *Components in Parallel*

For components in parallel, the opposite is true. Resistors and inductors add inversely, while capacitors add directly, as Figure 1.6 shows.

**Figure 1.6** Components in Parallel

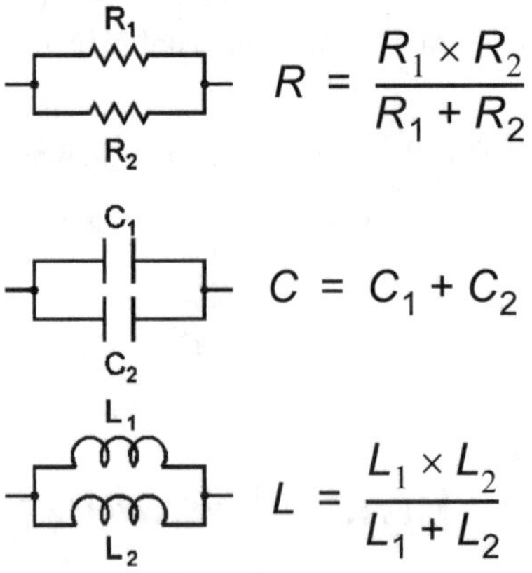

## *Resistive Dividers*

You can configure resistors to reduce voltage, either DC or AC. These circuits are called *attenuators*. A typical attenuator is shown in Figure 1.7.

**Figure 1.7** Resistive Attenuator

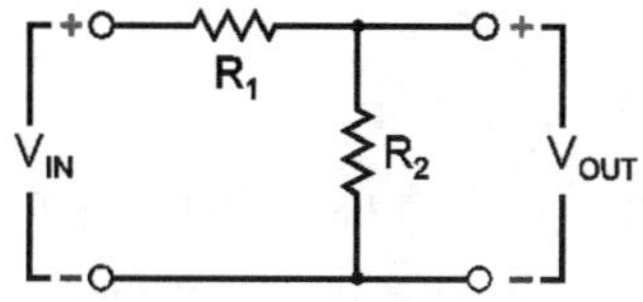


You can calculate the output voltage of the attenuator in Figure 1.7 as follows:

$$V_{out} = \frac{R_2}{R_1 + R_2} \times V_{in} \quad \textbf{Equation 1.10}$$

You can also determine the attenuation in dB using this formula:

$$Attenuation(dB) = 20 \times \log_{10} \frac{R_2}{R_1 + R_2} \quad \textbf{Equation 1.11}$$

If $R_1$ and $R_2$ are the same, $V_{out}$ is $0.5V_{in}$, and the signal is attenuated by 6dB. If $R_1$ is 900Ω and $R_2$ is 100Ω, $V_{out}$ is $0.1V_{in}$, and the signal is attenuated by 20dB.

## *Input and Output Impedance*

When used in actual circuits, all of the networks discussed above interact with other parts of the circuit, particularly those sections immediately before and after the network. These interactions can result in significant changes in performance. We can predict the effects of other circuitry if we know the input and output impedances of the network and its neighboring circuitry.

A network consumes a current when a voltage is applied to its input. The *input* or *load* impedance determines the current, and can be resistive, capacitive, inductive, or a combination of any of the three. One way to calculate input impedance is to "look" into the input of the network and "see" what impedance is there.

**Figure 1.8** Input and Output Impedance

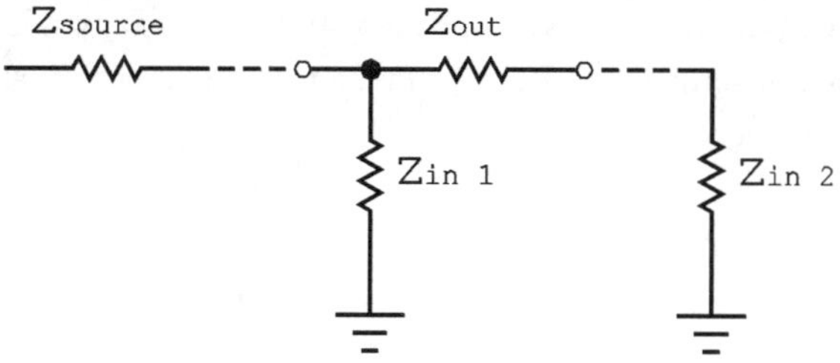


The network shown in Figure 1.8 has an input impedance $Z_{in1}$, which is fed by a previous stage whose *output impedance* is $Z_{source}$. The *output* or *source* impedance of a network is the resistance of its output terminals to the flow of current. You can see that $Z_{in1}$ and $Z_{source}$ form a voltage divider, so, if the output voltage of the previous stage is $V_{out}$, the input voltage $V_{in}$ of the network will be:

$$V_{in} = \frac{Z_{in1}}{Z_{in1} + Z_{source}} \times V_{ou} \quad \textbf{Equation 1.12}$$

If $Z_{source}$ is 50kΩ (typical for a preamp stage) and $Z_{in1}$ is 100kΩ (typical for a tone control circuit), then $V_{in} = \frac{100k}{100k + 50k} \times V_{out}$, or .67$V_{out}$. In this example, the signal is attenuated by about 3.5 dB; you can see that the effect of the output impedance can be significant.

In Figure 1.8, $Z_{out}$ forms a voltage divider with $Z_{in2}$, the input impedance of the following network. If the output voltage of the network is $V_{out}$, then the input voltage to the following network $V_{in2} = \frac{Z_{in2}}{Z_{out} + Z_{in2}} \times V_{out}$, as in Equation 1.12 above.

Let's calculate the input and output impedance of the dividing network of Fig. 1.7.

If you look into the input, you see a total resistance of $R_1 + R_2$. However, even though the input impedance of the network in isolation is $R_1 + R_2$, the network is always connected to another circuit, which affects its input impedance. If the other circuit's input impedance is $Z_l$, $Z_l$ is in parallel with $R_2$ and the network's input impedance ("$Z_i$") becomes:

$$Z_i = R_1 + \frac{Z_l \times R_2}{Z_l + R_2} \quad \textbf{Equation 1.13}$$

If $Z_l$ is comparable to $R_2$, the output of the network is changed as in Equation 1.13. In many circuits $Z_l$ is very high, in which case:

$$Z_i = R_1 + R_2 \quad \textbf{Equation 1.14},$$

and we can ignore the effect of $Z_l$.

You can calculate output impedance in the same way as input impedance, that is, by determining the impedance you see when you look into the output. The output impedance of the network in Figure 1.7 is $R_2$, assuming nothing is connected to the input of the network. However, something is always connected to the input, and this affects the output impedance. Assuming the output impedance of the circuit driving the network is $Z_s$, the output impedance ("$Z_o$") of the network is then $R_2$ in parallel with $R_1 + Z_s$. In many circuits (but not all) $Z_s$ is low and can be neglected, in which case:

$$Z_o = \frac{R_2 \times R_1}{R_2 + R_1} \quad \textbf{Equation 1.15}$$

You can generally ignore the effect of source and load impedances on circuit performance if the source impedance is at least 10 times lower than the input impedance, and the load impedance is at least 10 times higher than the output impedance. This is known as the "Rule of 10." So, if $R_1$ and $R_2$ are 10kΩ, to avoid affecting the attenuator's performance the maximum source impedance driving the attenuator should be $\frac{10k + 10k}{10} = 2k\Omega$, and the minimum load impedance should be $\frac{10k \times 10k}{10k + 10k} \times 10 = 50k\Omega$.

Many networks have input or output impedances that are frequency-dependant, usually because of capacitance in the network.

## *Frequency-dependent Dividing Networks*

The performance of resistive dividing networks does not change with frequency. However, dividing networks that incorporate capacitors or inductors are frequency-dependent, which is a useful property. Such networks are used extensively in guitar amplifiers, including in the tone control circuit, the gain stages, and the feedback circuit.

**Figure 1.9** High-pass Filter

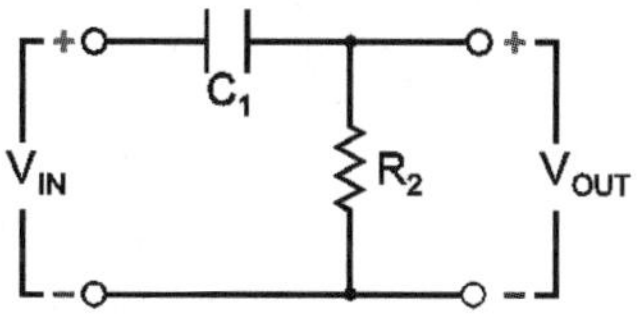


In Figure 1.9, we substitute a capacitor for the series resistor ($R_1$) of Figure 1.7. We can think of this circuit as a resistive voltage divider, where the impedance of the series element ($C_1$) varies with frequency. At very low frequencies, the impedance of $C_1$ is high, so the output of the attenuator is low. At very high frequencies, the impedance of $C_1$ is low, so the output of the attenuator is high. Because we are using a capacitor, both the amplitude and the phase of the output signal are affected. The formula for the amplitude of the output voltage is:

$$V_{out}(amplitude) = \frac{1}{\sqrt{1 + \left(\frac{1}{2\Pi f R_2 C_1}\right)^2}} \times V_{in} \quad \textbf{Equation 1.16}$$

The formula for the phase of the output signal is:

$$V_{out}(phase) = \tan^{-1} \frac{1}{2\Pi f R_2 C_1} \quad \textbf{Equation 1.17}$$

Let's calculate the amplitude and phase response of this circuit at various frequencies. First, let's choose values for $C_1$ and $R_2$. To start, we'll make $C_1$ = 100nf (100 x 10-9 farads) and $R_2$ = 10kΩ (10,000 ohms). Equation 1.16 then becomes:

$$V_{out}(amplitude) = \frac{1}{\sqrt{1+\left(\frac{1}{0.00628f}\right)^2}} \times V_{in}$$ **Equation 1.18**

Equation 1.17 becomes:

$$V_{out}(phase) = \tan^{-1}\frac{1}{0.00628f}$$ **Equation 1.19**

Let's make a table of output voltage and phase at several frequencies. We assume that $V_{in}$ = 1V to make things as simple as possible. We start at 20Hz and increase the frequency by octaves, and show the amplitude results in volts and in dB referenced to $V_{in}$ (1V). The phase results are in degrees.

**Table 1.2** Frequency Response Data of Network in Figure 1.9

| Frequency (Hz) | Vout (volts) | dB | Phase (degrees) |
|---|---|---|---|
| 20 | 0.12 | -18 | 83 |
| 40 | 0.24 | -12 | 76 |
| 80 | 0.45 | -7.0 | 63 |
| 160 | 0.71 | -3.0 | 45 |
| 320 | 0.90 | -1.0 | 26 |
| 640 | 0.97 | -0.2 | 14 |
| 1280 | 0.99 | -0.1 | 7.1 |
| 2560 | 1.0 | 0 | 3.6 |
| 5120 | 1.0 | 0 | 1.8 |
| 10240 | 1.0 | 0 | 0.9 |

We can see immediately that the output increases with frequency, so this network is a *high-pass filter* (*HPF*). The phase response goes from +83 degrees at 20Hz to 0.9 degrees at 10,240Hz, also typical of a high-pass filter. We can learn more about its performance by plotting the amplitude response, with frequency (in octaves) on the x-axis and level (in dB) on the y-axis, as in Figure 1.10.

**Figure 1.10** Frequency Response Plot of HPF in Figure 1.9

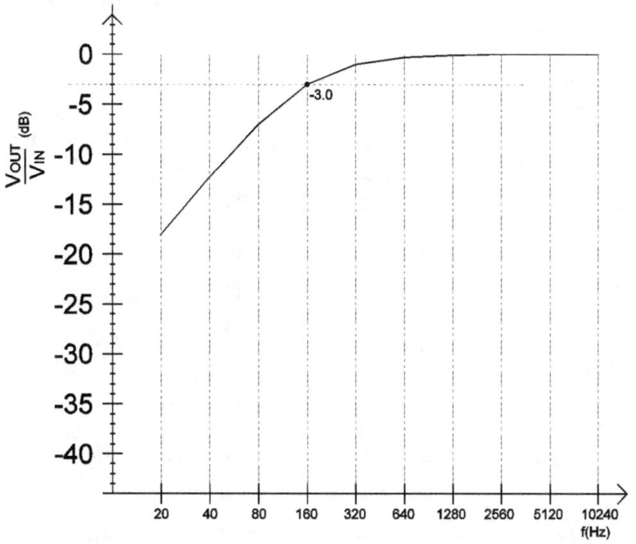


Filter characteristics of interest include the *cut-off* frequency, and the *slope*. The cut-off frequency is the frequency at which the filter's output has decreased by 3dB. Referring to Table 1.2 or Figure 1.10, you can see that the cut-off frequency is 160Hz. Again referring to Table 1.2, you can see that the phase response at the cut-off frequency is 45 degrees, halfway between the phase response at low and high frequencies. This is typical of filters with one capacitor or inductor, which are known as *first-order* filters. We can calculate the cut-off frequency using the formula:

$$f = \frac{1}{2\Pi R_2 C_1} \quad \textbf{Equation 1.20.}$$

In Figure 1.10, the area below the cut-off frequency is called the *stop-band*, because frequencies in this area are attenuated. The area above the cut-off frequency is called the *pass-band*, because frequencies in this area pass through the filter. The *slope* of the frequency response curve in the stop-band measures the filter's effectiveness at rejecting unwanted frequencies. First-order filters have a slope of 6dB per octave. That is, for every octave change in frequency, the filter's output changes by 6dB. In Table 1.2, you can see that our HPF reaches this slope in the lowest octave.

Let's see what happens when we change component values. If we lower the value of the capacitor, its impedance increases, so the cut-off frequency increases. Changing $C_1$ to 10nf changes Equation 1.18 to:

$$V_{out}(amplitude) = \frac{1}{\sqrt{1+\left(\frac{1}{0.000628f}\right)^2}} \times V_{in} \quad \textbf{Equation 1.21}$$

Equation 1.19 becomes:

$$V_{out}(phase) = \tan^{-1}\frac{1}{0.000628f}$$ **Equation 1.22**

The frequency response of our new HPF is now:

**Table 1.3** HPF Frequency Response, $C_1$ = 10nf, $R_2$ = 10kΩ

| Frequency (Hz) | Vout (volts) | dB | Phase (degrees) |
|---|---|---|---|
| 20 | 0.013 | -38 | 89 |
| 40 | 0.025 | -32 | 89 |
| 80 | 0.050 | -26 | 87 |
| 160 | 0.10 | -20 | 84 |
| 320 | 0.20 | -14 | 79 |
| 640 | 0.37 | -8.6 | 68 |
| 1280 | 0.63 | -4.1 | 51 |
| 2560 | 0.85 | -1.4 | 32 |
| 5120 | 0.95 | -0.4 | 17 |
| 10240 | 0.99 | -0.1 | 8.8 |

The data in Table 1.3 is plotted in Figure 1.11. As you can see, the cut-off frequency has increased, and is now about 1.6kHz. This is 10 times the cut-off frequency of our first HPF, since the value of $C_1$ has decreased by ten times. Also, note the 6dB/octave roll-off at low frequencies.

**Figure 1.11** HPF Response, $C_1$ = 10nf, $R_2$ = 10kΩ

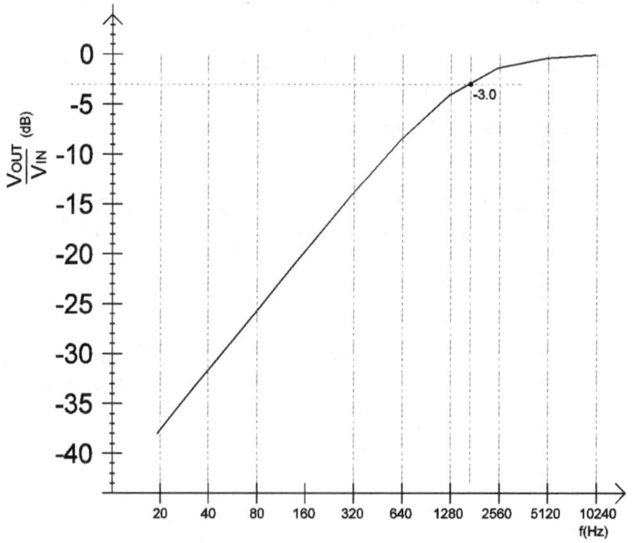

Now, let's increase $R_2$ to 100kΩ (with $C_1$ = 10nf). This HPF has the same response as the first example (with $R_2$ = 10kΩ and $C_1$ = 100nf), as shown in Figure 1.10. The terms of equations 1.18 and 1.19 remain the same, because $C_1$ decreases by a factor of 10 and $R_2$ increases by a factor of 10.

So, increasing $C_1$ or $R_2$ decreases the cut-off frequency, and decreasing $C_1$ or $R_2$ increases the cut-off frequency.

**Figure 1.12** Low-pass Filter

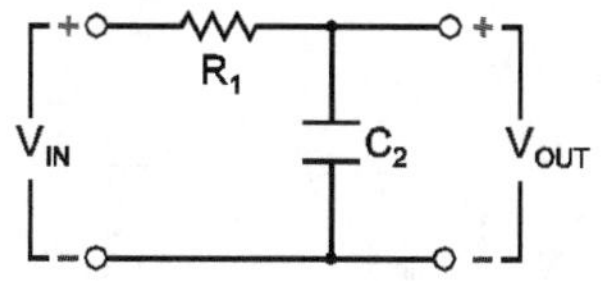


If we exchange the locations of the resistor and capacitor, as shown in Figure 1.12, the network becomes a *low-pass filter* (*LPF*). We can also think of this circuit as a voltage divider, where the impedance of the shunt element $C_2$ (the element connected to ground) varies with frequency. At low frequencies, the impedance of $C_2$ is high, so the output of the attenuator is high. At high frequencies, the impedance of $C_2$ is low, so the output of the attenuator is low. The equations describing its response are now:

$$V_{out}(amplitude) = \frac{1}{\sqrt{1+(2\Pi f R_1 C_2)^2}} \times V_{in} \quad \textbf{Equation 1.23}$$

$$V_{out}(phase) = -\tan^{-1} 2\Pi f R_1 C_2 \quad \textbf{Equation 1.24}$$

If $R_1$ = 10kΩ and $C_2$ = 100nf, equations 1.23 and 1.24 become:

$$V_{out}(amplitude) = \frac{1}{\sqrt{1+(0.00628f)^2}} \times V_{in} \quad \textbf{Equation 1.25}$$

$$V_{out}(phase) = -\tan^{-1} 0.00628f \quad \textbf{Equation 1.26}$$

The response is shown in Table 1.4.

The data in Table 1.4 is plotted in Figure 1.13. The cut-off frequency is again 160Hz and the slope is 6dB/octave.

We can calculate the effect of changing LPF component values in the same way as we did for the HPF. Increasing $C_2$ or $R_1$ decreases the cut-off frequency, and decreasing $C_2$ or $R_1$ increases the cut-off frequency.

**Table 1.4** LPF Response, $R_1 = 10K\Omega$, $C_2 = 100nf$

| Frequency (Hz) | Vout (volts) | dB | Phase (degrees) |
|---|---|---|---|
| 20 | 1.0 | 0 | -7 |
| 40 | 0.97 | -0.3 | -14 |
| 80 | 0.88 | -1.1 | -27 |
| 160 | 0.71 | -3.0 | -45 |
| 320 | 0.45 | -7.0 | -64 |
| 640 | 0.24 | -12 | -76 |
| 1280 | 0.12 | -18 | -83 |
| 2560 | 0.06 | -24 | -86 |
| 5120 | 0.03 | -30 | -88 |
| 10240 | 0.02 | -36 | -89 |

**Figure 1.13** LPF Frequency Response

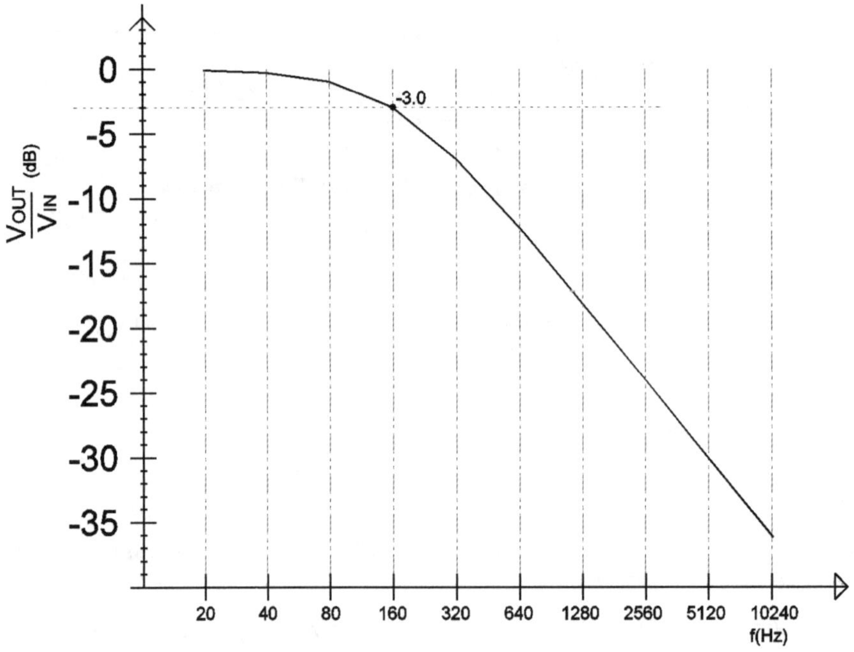


The formula for the LPF cut-off frequency is similar to the one used for the HPF (Equation 1.20):

$$f = \frac{1}{2\Pi R_1 C_2}.$$ **Equation 1.27**

Many other circuits are possible. If you use more reactive components (capacitors or inductors), you can increase the slope of the filter, which is useful in many applications, such as equalizers. In general, the more complex the filter, the more phase shift it introduces.

## Kirchhoff's Laws

In 1845 Gustav Kirchhoff described two laws which are widely used in electronic circuit design and analysis.

*Kirchhoff's Voltage Law* (abbreviated *KVL*) states that the sum of all voltages around a closed loop equals zero. This concept is illustrated in Figure 1.14.

**Figure 1.14** Kirchhoff's Voltage Law

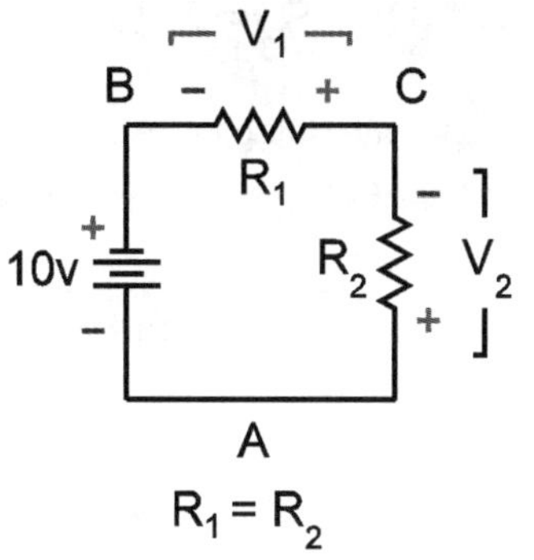


In Figure 1.14, three components, a 10V battery and two 10Ω resistors, are connected in a closed loop. By KVL, the sum 10V + V1 + V2 equals zero. Furthermore, because the two resistors are of equal value, the voltage across each resistor is the same, since the same current flows through both resistors. So, we can rewrite the KVL equation as:

$$10V + 2 \times V_1 = 0 \text{, or}$$

$$2 \times V_1 = -10V \text{, or } V_1 = -5V .$$

Noting the polarity marked in Figure 1.14, we can see that the voltage from point C to point B is -5V, so the voltage from point B to point C is 5V. Since $V_1$ equals $V_2$, the voltage from point C to point A is also 5V. To put it another way, the battery voltage is divided equally between $R_1$ and $R_2$, each of which has 5V across it.

*Kirchhoff's Current Law* (abbreviated *KCL*) states that the sum of all currents entering a circuit node is zero. A circuit node is any point where various components are connected. Another way of saying this is that the sum of all currents leaving a node must equal the sum of all currents entering the node.

**Figure 1.15** Kirchhoff's Current Law

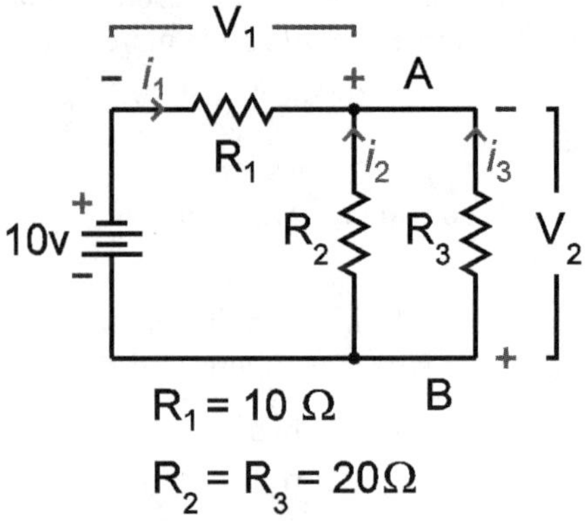


In Figure 1.15, the sum of the currents entering point A ($I_1$ - $I_2$ - $I_3$) equals zero. $V_1$ is the voltage across $R_1$, and $V_2$ is the voltage across $R_2$ and $R_3$. We can see from Ohm's Law that:

$I_1 = \frac{10 - V_2}{R_1}$ **Equation 1.28,** $I_2 = \frac{V_2}{R_2}$ **Equation 1.29**, and $I_3 = \frac{V_2}{R_3}$ **Equation 1.30**.

Substituting, we have:

$$\frac{10 - V_2}{R_1} - \frac{V_2}{R_2} - \frac{V_2}{R_3} = 0 \quad \textbf{Equation 1.31}$$

Since $R_1$ = 10Ω and $R_2$ = $R_3$ = 20Ω:

$$\frac{10 - V_2}{10} - \frac{V_2}{20} - \frac{V_2}{20} = 0 \quad \textbf{Equation 1.32}$$

Solving, we get $V_2$ = 5V. Thus, $I_2$ = $I_3$ = 5V/20Ω = 0.25A, and $I_1 = \frac{10 - 5}{10} = 0.5A$, and $V_1$ = 5V.

## Rectification

*Rectifiers* convert AC to DC. We use them in the power supply to convert the AC voltage from the power system to the DC voltages used in the amplifier. We can implement rectifiers with solid-state devices or using vacuum tubes (both are called *diodes*).

A diode allows current to flow in only one direction. The schematic symbol for a solid-state diode is shown in Figure 1.16. Current flows from the anode to the cathode only when the voltage at the anode is higher than the voltage at the cathode.

**Figure 1.16** Diode

Figure 1.17 shows two waveforms. The upper waveform is 120Vrms, 60Hz from a wall outlet. The lower waveform is the same signal after it passes through a diode. Only the positive halves of the waveform pass through the diode, because, during the negative halves, the cathode is positive with respect to the anode. You can see that the average value of the waveform is now positive, while the average value of the AC input signal is zero. Although the signal still varies, we can now use it to create a DC voltage. Note that the peak voltage is 170V, which is the peak value of a 120Vrms sine wave.

**Figure 1.17** Half-wave Rectification

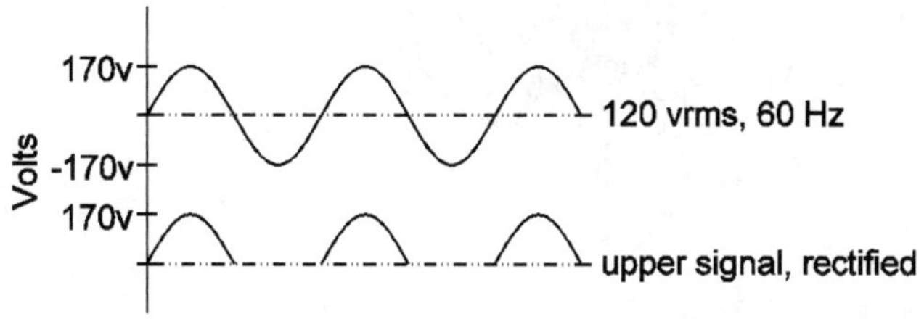


The process shown in Figure 1.17 is called *half-wave* rectification, because the diode only passes the positive half of the waveform.

*Full-wave* rectification uses both halves of the wave and thus provides a more balanced and efficient use of power. Figure 1.18 shows a full-wave bridge rectifier.

**Figure 1.18** Full-wave Bridge Rectifier

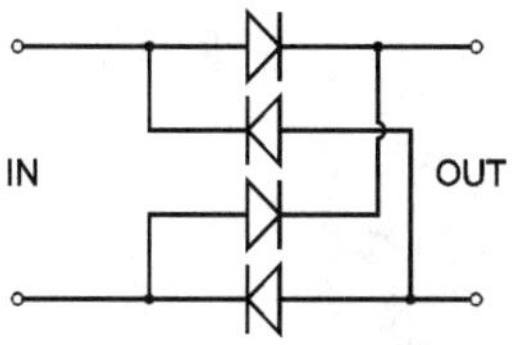


Figure 1.19 shows the output of the full-wave bridge rectifier.

**Figure 1.19** Full-wave Rectification

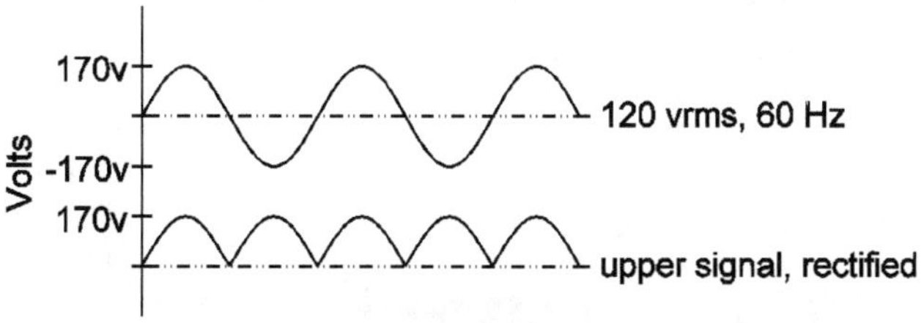


As you can see from Figures 1.17 and 1.19, the output of a rectifier is not smooth. We usually add a filter after the rectifier to further smooth the waveform. We will discuss rectifier and filter design further in Chapter 2.

## Transformers

As we discussed in the section on inductance, *transformers* are a special type of inductor. You may remember that passing a current through a coil of wire creates a magnetic field. The magnetic field extends out of the plane of the coil, as in Figure 1.20. The lines shown represent *magnetic flux*: the higher the flux density, the stronger the magnetic field.

**Figure 1.20** Magnetic Field Created by Current Passing Through a Coil

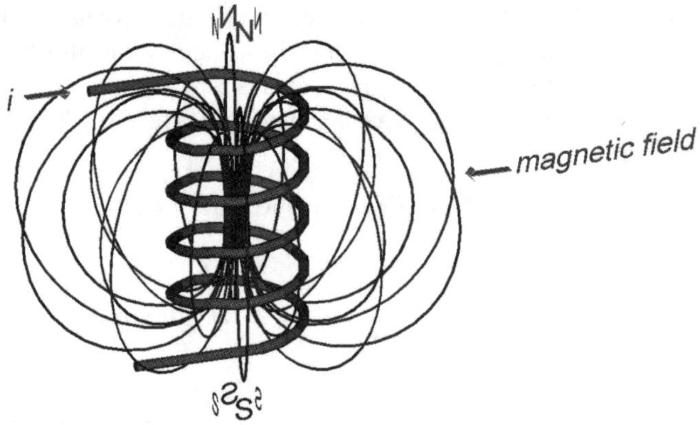


If you wrap the coil around a square ferrous metal core, as in Figure 1.21, the flux lines (for the most part) follow the core. The flux density (and therefore the inductance) of a coil with a ferrous core is substantially higher than the flux density of the same coil with an air (open) core.

Just as passing a current through a coil produces a magnetic field, passing a magnetic field through a coil produces a current. This is the theoretical basis of all transformers.

**Figure 1.21** Coil with Ferrous Core

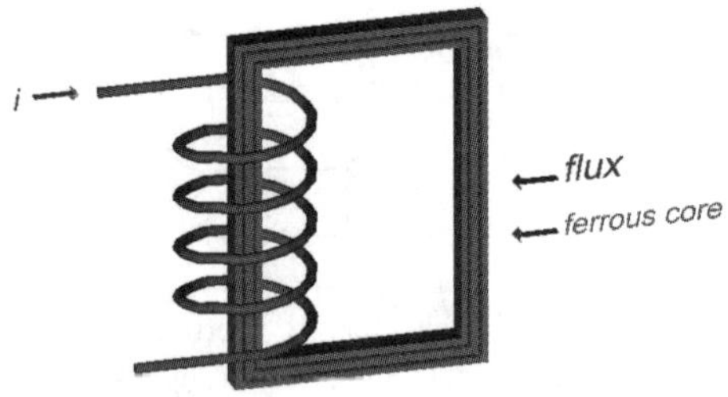


If we add a second coil to the ferrous core of Figure 1.21, as in Figure 1.22, the current $I_1$ flowing through coil A (known as the *primary* coil) induces magnetic flux in the core. The flux in turn induces a current $I_2$ in coil B (the *secondary* coil) that is proportional to the current flowing in coil A.

**Figure 1.22** Transformer

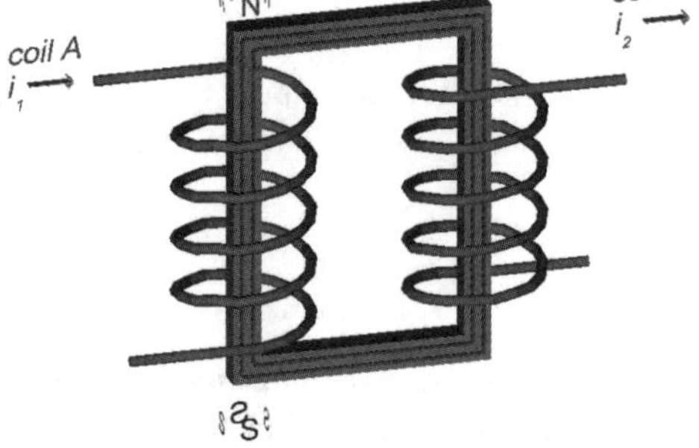

If the number of turns in coil A is $N_1$ and the number of turns in coil B is $N_2$, then:

$$I_2 = \frac{N_1}{N_2} \times I_1 \quad \textbf{Equation 1.33}$$

In an ideal transformer, the power in the secondary winding is the same as the power in the primary winding:

$$V_1 \times I_1 = V_2 \times I_2 \,. \quad \textbf{Equation 1.34}$$

Therefore, the ratio of the voltages in the windings is the inverse of the ratio of the currents:

$$V_2 = \frac{N_2}{N_1} \times V_1 \,. \quad \textbf{Equation 1.35}$$

Since the impedance $Z_1$ of the primary winding is $\frac{V_1}{I_1}$ and the impedance $Z_2$ of the secondary is $\frac{V_2}{I_2}$, we can divide Equation 1.35 by Equation 1.33 to obtain:

$$Z_2 = \left(\frac{N_2}{N_1}\right)^2 \times Z_1 \quad \textbf{Equation 1.36,}$$

We call $\frac{N_2}{N_1}$ the *turns ratio* of the transformer and $\left(\frac{N_2}{N_1}\right)^2$ the *impedance ratio*; they are key transformer parameters.

You can calculate the turns ratio if you know the impedances. For example, if you select an output transformer with a specified primary impedance of 10kΩ and secondary impedance of 4Ω, the turns ration is 50:1 (the square root of $\frac{10k}{4}$). Similarly, if a transformer has a turns ratio of 20:1, and you connect an 8Ω load to the secondary winding, the impedance of the primary winding is 3.2kΩ ($400 \times 8$). If you connect a 16Ω load to the same transformer, the primary impedance is 6.4kΩ.

Transformers can have more than one primary or secondary winding; we will see some examples later in this section. Windings can also be *tapped*, where connections are made to the winding at one or more points in addition to the beginning and end. If the winding is tapped in the middle, it is called *center-tapped.* Figure 1.23 shows the schematic symbol for a transformer with one primary winding and two center-tapped secondary windings.

**Figure 1.23** Transformer with one Primary and two Center-tapped Secondary Windings

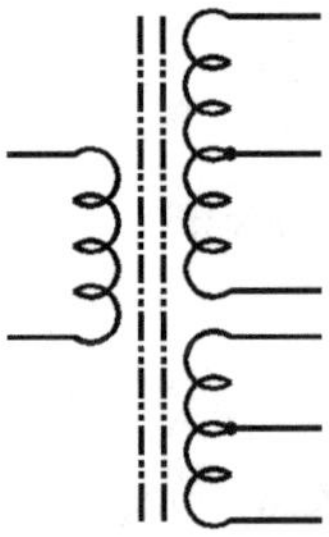

Two types of transformers are commonly used in guitar amplifiers. The *power* transformer has a primary winding that accepts household current and two or more secondary windings. The secondary windings are:

— A high-voltage winding, usually center-tapped. The center tap allows full-wave rectification using only two diodes, as we will see later. DC voltages used in amplifiers typically range from -60VDC to over 500VDC. The high-voltage winding often has another tap to provide a suitable voltage to bias the output stage.

— A 6.3VrmsAC winding. This winding is often center-tapped, and is used to heat the tube filaments, as discussed in the next section.

— If tube rectification is used, an additional filament winding (usually 5VrmsAC) is required for the rectifier tube filament. Tube rectifiers are discussed further in the power supply section of Chapter 2.

Figure 1.23 shows a typical power transformer schematic symbol. The primary winding is on the left, and the two center-tapped secondary windings are on the right.

Power transformers are specified according to the voltages and currents supplied by the secondary windings. For example, a transformer might supply 400Vrms AC at 100ma current and 6.3Vrms AC at 2A current. The transformer may also have additional primary windings, for example, to support 220VAC.

Most tube amplifiers also require an *output* transformer. As we will see later, the output transformer converts high-impedance, high-voltage power generated by the output stage to low-impedance, lower-voltage power required by the speakers.

The output transformer has one primary winding, which connects to the output stage, and one secondary winding, which connects to the speaker. The primary is center-tapped if the output stage is *push-pull*, as we discuss in Chapter 2. The secondary is often tapped to match speakers with different impedances. A typical output transformer schematic symbol is shown in Figure 1.24.

**Figure 1.24** Typical Output Transformer

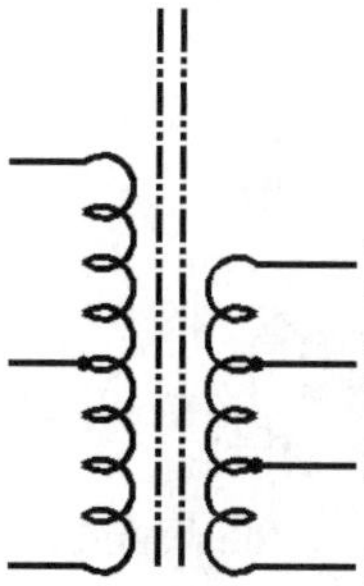


Output transformers are specified as follows:

— The impedance of the primary winding, and whether it is center-tapped. You will learn how to choose the correct primary impedance in Chapter 2.

— The impedance of the secondary, and whether additional taps are required. Some output transformers have a single 4Ω secondary, while others have 4Ω, 8Ω, and 16Ω taps.

— The power handling capability and frequency response bandwidth of the transformer. Transformers for high-power amplifiers are larger than those for smaller amplifiers, because they must handle more current, voltage, and magnetic flux. In addition, as we will see later, we need a larger transformer to obtain full power at low frequencies.

Note that there is no electrical connection between the windings in a transformer. Therefore, there is no theoretical limitation on the DC potential difference that can exist between windings. For example, one secondary winding of a power transformer can be at 400VDC while another can be at 0VDC. We will discuss this concept further in the power supply section of Chapter 2.

Transformer manufacturers consider several other factors when designing transformers, including the size and characteristics of the core, the number of turns in each coil, the way the coils are wound on the core, and the wire and insulation used for each coil. These factors affect power handling, efficiency, frequency response, and other performance characteristics.

# Tubes

This section covers how tubes work and their basic characteristics. Tube amplifier circuits are discussed in Chapter 2.

## *Diodes*

The diode is the simplest type of tube. It is called a diode because it has two elements: the cathode, which emits electrons, and the plate, which collects electrons. The schematic symbol for a tube diode is shown in Figure 1.25. Tube diodes are used in the power supply of some amplifiers to convert AC to DC, where they are known as rectifiers.

**Figure 1.25** Tube Diode Schematic Symbol

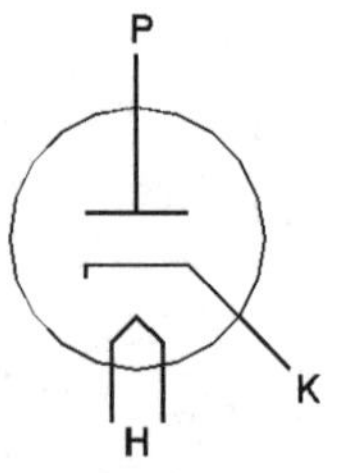


In Figure 1.25, the plate is marked *P*, the cathode *K*, and the two leads marked *H* are the *heater*, also called the *filament*. The filament heats the cathode, which then emits electrons. In some diodes, including the rectifier tubes most commonly used in amplifiers, the heater is connected directly to the cathode. This is called a *directly-heated* cathode and requires one less connection to the tube. Other diodes are *indirectly-heated*, meaning that the cathode and filament connections are independent.

When the cathode is heated, a cloud of electrons forms near its surface. If the plate voltage is positive with respect to the cathode, the electrons in the cloud are attracted to the plate and flow from the cathode to the plate. So, conventional current flows from the plate to the cathode, as explained earlier. However, if the plate is negative with respect to the cathode, the electrons are repelled by the plate and no current flows. Thus, the tube behaves as a rectifier, exactly as described earlier. You can find details on tube rectification in Chapter 2.

## *Triodes*

Triodes add a third element, known as the *control grid*, physically located between the plate and cathode. Electrons traveling from the cathode to the plate pass through the control grid.

The schematic symbol for a triode is shown in Figure 1.26. The control grid is marked *G*, and the other elements are marked as in Figure 1.25.

**Figure 1.26** Tube Triode Schematic Symbol

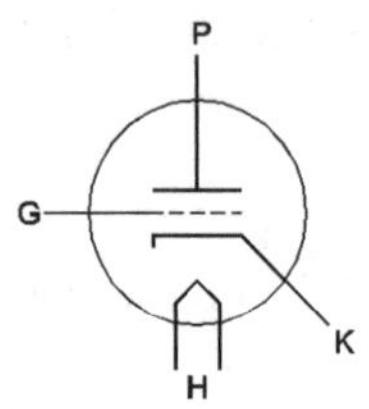


As in a diode, electrons emitted by the cathode flow to the plate if the plate is more positive than the cathode. We can control this current by making the control grid negative with respect to the cathode. In this case, the electrons are repelled by the negative control grid and cannot reach the plate, so plate current decreases. The more negative the grid voltage, the less current flows. Triodes are normally operated with the grid voltage negative with respect to the cathode.

If the control grid is at the same potential as the cathode, it has little or no effect on plate current. If it is positive with respect to the cathode, current flows from the cathode to the grid as well as to the plate.

**Figure 1.27** Triode Operation with Cathode Grounded

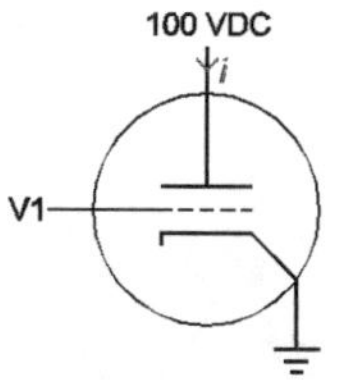


Figure 1.27 shows a triode with 100VDC on the plate, the cathode grounded, and a negative DC voltage $V_1$ at the control grid. If $V_1$ is -1V, the plate current I is 10mA. If we lower $V_1$ to -1.5V, the plate current decreases to 5mA. If we continue to lower $V_1$, the plate current stops entirely. The voltage at which the plate current stops is known as the *cut-off voltage.*

If we raise $V_1$ to -0.5V, the plate current increases to 15mA. If we continue to raise $V_1$, electrons begin to flow to the grid in addition to the plate, an undesirable condition.

The upper curve of Figure 1.28 shows the control grid voltage changing from -1V to -1.5V to -0.5V and then back to -1V. The lower curve shows the corresponding change in plate current from 10mA to 5mA to 15mA and back to 10mA.

Now, suppose we apply an AC voltage to the control grid, as in Figure 1.29. The plate current follows the grid voltage. This is how a properly designed triode amplifier stage reacts to an audio signal.

**Figure 1.28** Plate Current vs. Control Grid Voltage #1

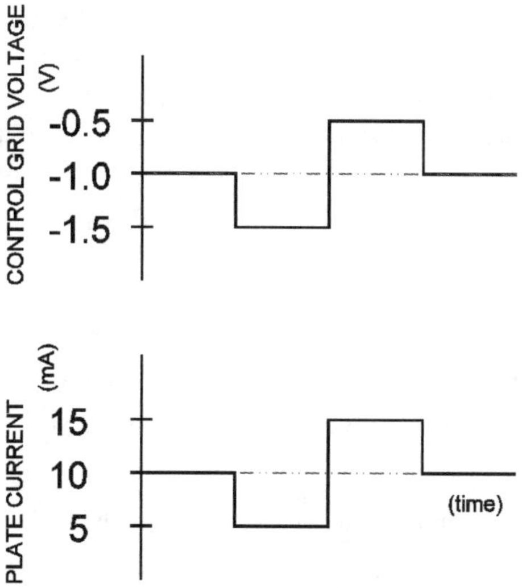

**Figure 1.29** Plate Current vs. Control Grid Voltage #2

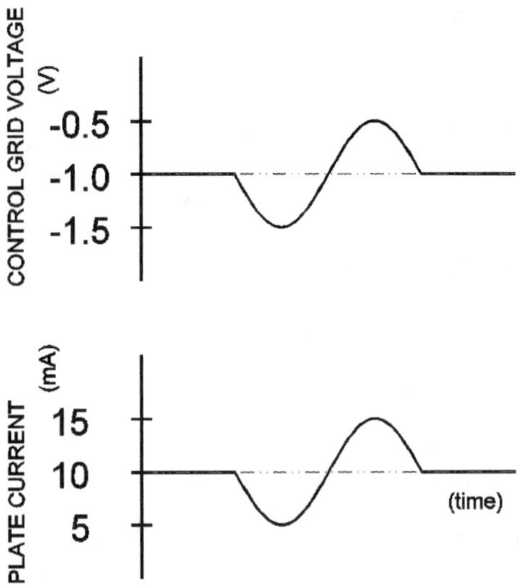


We can thus control plate current by varying grid voltage. The plate current also depends on the plate voltage. As the plate voltage increases, the plate current also increases, since the plate attracts more electrons from the cathode.

The relationship between control grid voltage and plate current for a given plate voltage is a fundamental property of a tube. Figure 1.30 shows the relationship between plate current and control grid voltage for a typical triode tube at several plate voltages. Looking at the curve for $V_P = 300V$, you can see that the cut-off voltage is about -18V, and that there is a fairly linear relationship between control grid voltage and plate current from -13V to -10V. So, if you design a linear amplifier stage with this device and choose a plate voltage of 300V, you should operate the stage with the control grid between -13V and -10V. Operating outside this range creates distortion.

---

### Measuring Tube Characteristics

A triode has three elements, so we can measure its characteristics in a number of ways, including:

- We maintain one or more of the elements at a constant DC voltage, which can be positive, negative, or ground.
- We maintain a constant current into or out of one or more elements.
- We leave one or more elements "open," allowing the current and voltage to vary freely, and measure the voltage or current at the elements.

Because there are three elements and three different possible conditions (open, constant current, or constant voltage), there are many possible ways to approach measuring the characteristics. One common approach is to fix (that is, hold constant) the voltage or current of one element, vary the voltage or current of a second element, and measure the current or voltage of the third element. That is the approach taken in measuring tube characteristics.

---

**Figure 1.30** Plate Current vs. Grid Voltage, Family of Curves

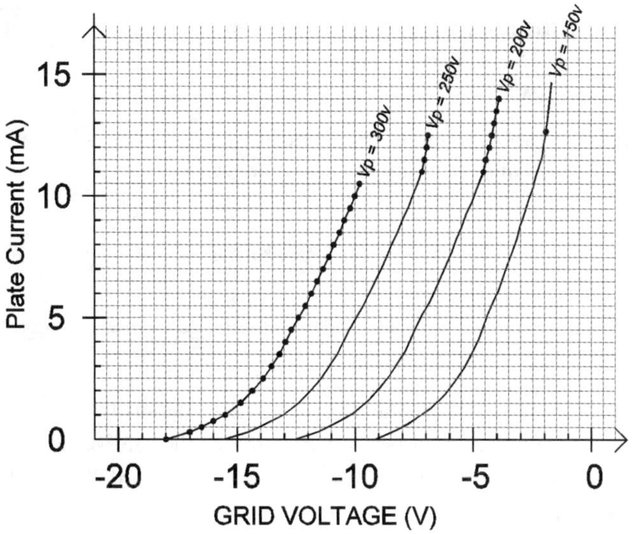


As you can see from Figure 1.30, three parameters are varying: plate current, plate voltage, and control grid voltage. Figure 1.31 shows the same data in a different way, with plate voltage on the x-axis, plate current on the y-axis, and each curve representing one control grid voltage. Tube data sheets usually present the data in this form. Remember, Figure 1.31 shows the same data as Figure 1.30, just presented differently.

**Figure 1.31** Plate Current vs. Plate Voltage, Family of Curves

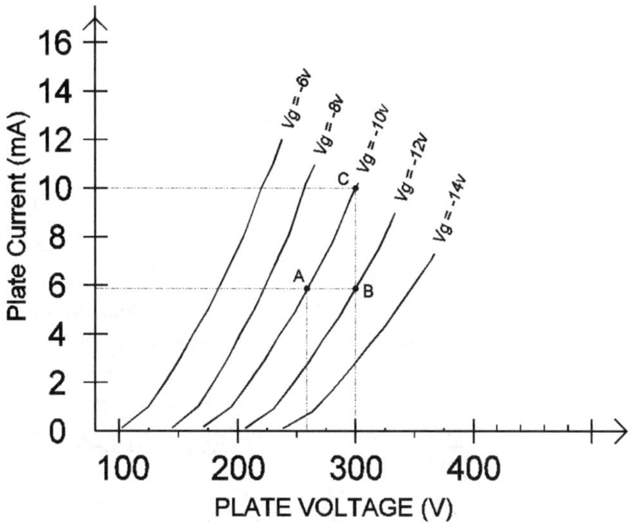


In Chapter 2, we use these *characteristic curves* to design amplifier stages.

## *Tube Constants*

We can use the characteristic curves to derive *tube constants*, which are important characteristics unique to each tube. These characteristics include the *amplification factor*, *AC plate resistance*, and *transconductance*.

The amplification factor (abbreviated μ, pronounced "mu") measures how much the plate voltage changes for a given change in grid voltage. To be precise,

$$\mu = \frac{\Delta V_p}{\Delta V_g}$$ **Equation 1.37**,

where $\Delta V_p$ is the change in plate voltage, $\Delta V_g$ is the change in grid voltage, and plate current is held constant.

Referring to Figure 1.31, note points A and B. At point A, the grid voltage is –10V, the plate voltage is 260V, and the plate current is 6mA. At point B, the grid voltage is –12V, the plate voltage is 300V, and the plate current is also 6mA. So, with the plate current held constant at 6mA, a 40V change in plate voltage (300 – 260) corresponds to a 2V change in grid voltage (12 - 10). Therefore,

$$\mu = \frac{40V}{2V} = 20\,.$$ **Equation 1.38**

Another important tube constant is the AC plate resistance $r_p$, which represents the internal resistance of the tube to an AC signal. We know from Ohm's Law that $R = \frac{V}{I}$, so $r_p$ is defined as:

$$r_p = \frac{\Delta V_p}{\Delta I_p}$$ **Equation 1.39**, where

$\Delta I_p$ is the change in plate current, $\Delta V_p$ is the change in plate voltage, and the grid voltage is held constant. At point A in Figure 1.31, the plate voltage is 260V, the plate current is 6mA, and the grid voltage is -10V. At point C, the plate voltage is 300V, the plate current is 10mA, and the grid voltage is also -10V. So, with the grid voltage held constant at -10V, a change of 40V in plate voltage (300 - 260) corresponds to a change of 4mA in plate current (10 – 6). Therefore,

$$r_p = \frac{40V}{.004A} = 10{,}000\Omega$$ **Equation 1.40**.

The third important tube constant is the transconductance $g_m$, with units of *mhos*. Mhos are the inverse of ohms, and are obtained when we divide current by voltage. Transconductance is defined as:

$$g_m = \frac{\Delta I_p}{\Delta V_g}$$ **Equation 1.41**, where

$\Delta I_p$ and $\Delta V_p$ are as previously defined, and plate voltage is held constant.

At point B in Figure 1.31, plate current is 6mA, grid voltage is -12V, and plate voltage is 300V. At point C, plate current is 10mA, grid voltage is -10V, and plate voltage is also 300V. So, with the plate voltage held constant at 300V, a change of 4mA in plate current (10 – 6) corresponds to a change of 2V in grid voltage (12 – 10). Therefore,

$$g_m = \frac{.004A}{2V} = .002mhos. \quad \textbf{Equation 1.42}$$

Amplification factor, plate resistance, and transconductance are related according to the following formula:

$$\mu = r_p \times g_m. \quad \textbf{Equation 1.43}$$

Therefore, if you know two of the constants, you can calculate the third.

In Chapter 2 we will use these tube characteristics to design amplifier circuits.

## *Pentodes*

Pentodes have five elements, as their name implies. The two additional elements are the *suppressor grid* and the *screen grid.* Both are located between the control grid and the plate, with the suppressor grid closest to the plate. The additional grids give pentodes a higher amplification factor (μ) than triodes, make plate current relatively independent of plate voltage, and offer advantages in high-frequency circuits. The schematic symbol for a pentode is shown in Figure 1.32.

**Figure 1.32** Pentode Tube Schematic Symbol

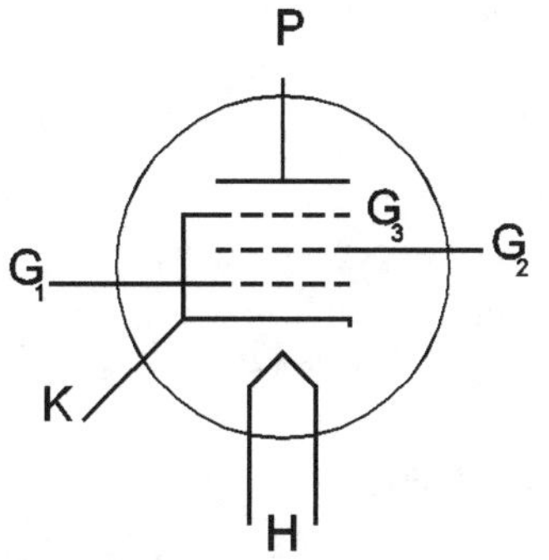


The suppressor grid is normally connected to the cathode, sometimes inside the tube and sometimes externally, making the pentode functionally a four-element device. The possible uses of the screen grid are discussed in Chapter 2.

Typical pentode characteristics are shown in Figure 1.33. Note the flatness of the curves as compared to the triode characteristics shown in Figure 1.31. For a triode, plate current increases linearly with plate voltage. For a pentode, plate current is essentially independent of plate voltage.

All of the output tubes we will discuss are pentodes, while all of the preamplifier tubes are triodes, because the majority of guitar amplifier designs use triodes for the preamplifier stages and pentodes for the output stage, although you can use either type of tube in either application. However, pentodes often have too much gain to be effective in preamplifier stages, and they are usually noisier and more *microphonic* (creating electrical noise when mechanically shocked) than triodes. True triode output tubes are more expensive and limited than pentode tubes; you can connect pentodes to operate as triodes if desired.

**Figure 1.33** Typical Pentode Plate Current vs. Plate Voltage Family of Curves

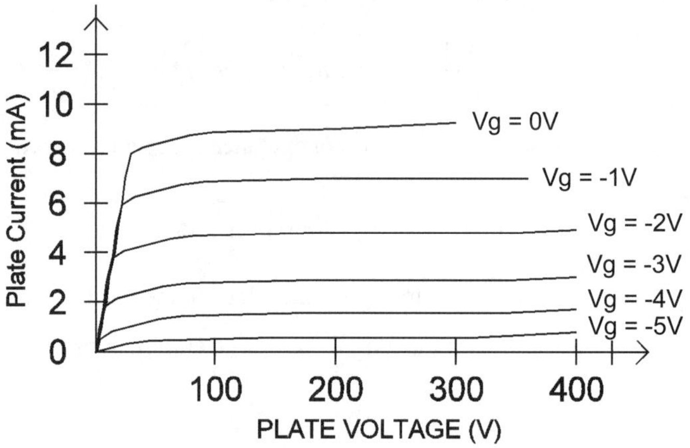


## Ground

The term *ground* refers to a point of zero potential. It originated when electrical and electronic equipment was literally grounded, that is, tied to a metal rod stuck in the ground. Modern equipment is grounded through the electrical distribution system using the third pin of the electrical plug. Note the schematic symbol for ground in Figure 1.27.

DC voltages are referenced to ground, so when we say "100VDC," for example, we mean that the DC potential at a certain point in the circuit is 100V with respect to ground. AC voltages can be referenced to ground or to a DC voltage, as we discuss in the next section.

We must consider several ground references in amplifiers, including the metal chassis, the input and output connectors, and the copper ground traces on printed circuit boards. Failure to properly ground results in *ground loops*, which are currents induced by different ground potentials that cause hum and noise. We will discuss grounding in detail in Chapter 4.

## Characteristics of Signals

### *AC and DC Signals*

As we have already seen, both DC and AC signals appear in amplifiers.

DC voltages include power supply voltages for various stages of the amplifier, and control voltages used for circuits such as channel switching. Pure DC voltages have a frequency of 0Hz. For this reason, capacitors "block" DC voltages. That is, a DC voltage at one side of a capacitor does not pass through to the other side. Resistors and inductors do not block DC voltages.

Audio signals are AC voltages. This includes the input signal to the amplifier from the guitar pickup, all inter-stage signals, and the output signal at the speaker terminals.

AC signals can "ride" on DC voltages. For example, if we add a 10VAC signal to a 40VDC signal, we obtain the composite signal shown in Figure 1.34. Since capacitors block DC, if we pass this signal through a capacitor, we can isolate the AC component from the DC component.

**Figure 1.34** Signal with DC and AC Components

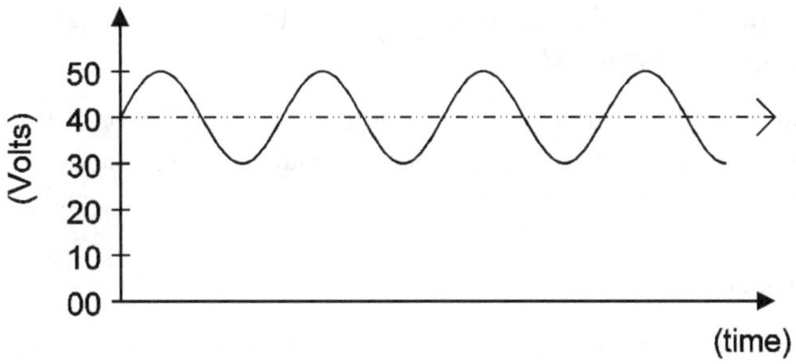


## *AC Signal Amplitude*

We can describe the amplitude of an AC signal in several ways. The *peak-to-peak* amplitude is the voltage difference between the top of the positive half and the bottom of the negative half of the wave. In Figure 1.34, the peak-to-peak amplitude of the AC signal is 20V. The *peak* amplitude is half of the peak-to-peak amplitude. In Figure 1.34, the peak amplitude is 10V. The *root-mean-square* or *rms* amplitude describes the voltage's ability to create power compared to a DC voltage. The difference between peak and rms voltages depends on the shape of the signal. For a sine wave, the rms voltage is .707 times the peak voltage. Thus, the rms amplitude of the AC signal in Figure 1.34 is $7.07V_{rms}$.

We use rms voltages to calculate power. For example, we can calculate the output power of an amplifier. Recall that:

$$W = V \times I \text{ **Equation 1.1**, and } I = \frac{V}{R} \text{ **Equation 1.4**.}$$

We can substitute the second equation into the first to obtain:

$$W = V \times \frac{V}{R} = \frac{V^2}{R}. \text{ **Equation 1.44**}$$

If V is the peak voltage, Equation 1.44 yields the peak power. If V is the rms voltage, Equation 1.44 yields the *average* (sometimes erroneously referred to as *rms*) power. If V is the peak voltage of a sine wave, the rms voltage is .707V, and the average power is:

$$W_{avg} = \frac{(0.707V)^2}{R} = 0.5\frac{V^2}{R}. \text{ **Equation 1.45**}$$

Thus, the average power is half the peak power for a sine wave.

AC signal levels vary widely in amplifiers. The maximum output of a guitar pickup may reach $1V_{rms}$, which can result in $15V_{rms}$ at the speaker output. Internal signal levels can exceed $100V_{rms}$ in some stages of the amplifier.

## The Superposition Principle

You've probably noticed that all of our signal-related analysis has been done using sine waves. Since guitar waveforms are much more complex it is reasonable to question whether results measured with sine waves apply to guitar signals. All audio signals can be made by adding sine waves. As long as the amplifier is operating linearly (that is, without distortion), we can determine the response to a sum of sine waves from the response to individual sine waves. This is known as the *superposition principle.*

The superposition principle does not apply to nonlinear systems, so once the amplifier begins distorting we must use other methods to predict and analyze performance. You will find a detailed discussion of distortion in Chapter 3.

## Noise and Distortion

All amplifiers produce and amplify noise. Noise includes hum from the 60Hz AC supply voltage, random noise from amplifier components, and noise from the guitar pickups and wiring. We can minimize the first two by proper design and grounding, while the third depends on the guitar and the environment.

You can think of distortion as any component in an output signal that does not exist in the input signal. By this definition, hum and noise are a type of distortion, which we usually try to minimize.

However, we may want to intentionally create other types of distortion. For example, guitar amplifiers create *harmonic* distortion by overdriving tube stages. Harmonic distortion components are integer multiples of the signal frequencies, and can sound quite musical.

*Inter-modulation* distortion (*IM*) is created when two or more signals interact to produce new signals at frequencies that are the sum and difference of the input frequencies. For example, if we amplify 100Hz and 160Hz through a distorted stage, it creates new frequencies at 60Hz (160 – 100) and 260Hz (160 + 100). If other frequencies are present, the stage creates many additional frequencies, and the sound becomes harsh and unmusical. In certain situations, such as power chords, IM distortion can be controlled and musical.

# Chapter 2
# Basic Amplifier Design

In this chapter, we first learn how tubes are used to amplify signals. We then discuss each circuit block used in a basic guitar amplifier and how the blocks are interconnected to form a functioning unit. We use the fundamental concepts described in Chapter 1 throughout; if you have trouble understanding anything, you can go back and review the relevant section.

## Triode Amplifier Stage

In this section, we discuss voltage amplification achieved using a triode tube, with the input signal applied to the grid and the output taken from the plate.

The basic triode voltage amplifier, shown in Figure 2.1, adds a *load* resistor ($R_L$) to the plate circuit. One end of the resistor is connected to the plate, and the other end is connected to a DC voltage source.

**Figure 2.1** Triode Amplifier Circuit

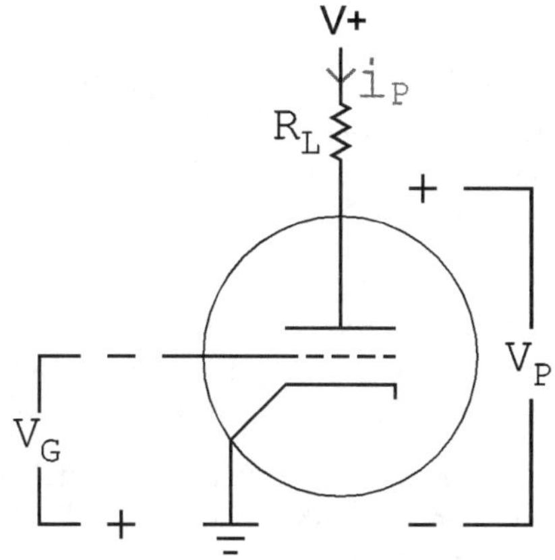


To understand how the triode amplifier works, first assume the grid voltage is sufficiently negative that no current flows from the plate to the cathode. In this case, the plate current is zero, so no voltage drops across $R_L$, and the plate voltage equals the supply voltage. Now raise the grid voltage until current begins to flow through $R_L$, resulting in a voltage drop across $R_L$. The voltage at the plate falls by the voltage dropped across $R_L$. If we raise the grid voltage further, current increases and the plate voltage decreases. Thus, an increase in grid voltage causes a decrease in plate voltage, and we have the foundation of a voltage amplifying stage.

Let's design a triode amplifier using the 12AX7A high-μ triode, whose characteristic curves are shown in Figure 2.2.

**Figure 2.2** 12AX7A Characteristic Curves

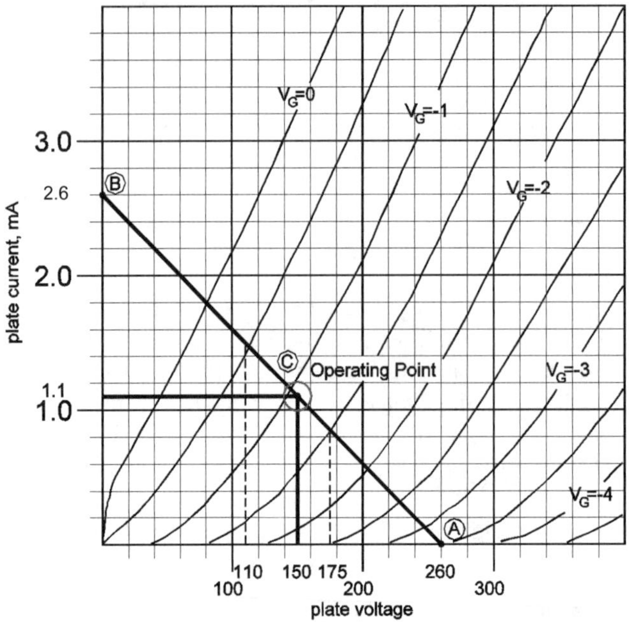


To start, we select a power supply voltage of 260V and a plate load resistor value of 100kΩ. Later in this section, we will see how changing $R_L$ and the power supply voltage affect the amplifier's performance.

We know that if the plate current is zero the voltage at the plate equals the power supply voltage, or 260V. Point A on Figure 2.2 represents this condition. If the plate is at zero volts, the maximum current that flows through $R_L$ (using Ohm's Law) is 2.6mA, as represented by point B. We now draw a straight line between points A and B; this line represents all possible combinations of plate voltage and current, and is called the *load line*. If we change either the supply voltage or $R_L$, the position of the load line changes.

Each point on the load line corresponds to a particular grid voltage. If the grid is sufficiently negative, the tube is at cut-off, and no current flows in the plate (point A). If the grid voltage is sufficiently positive, current flows from the grid to the cathode. Both of these conditions cause distortion, so in most cases, we want to operate the stage between these two extremes.

Next we select the *operating point* on the load line AB. In normal operation, the grid is biased to the negative DC voltage corresponding to the operating point. The input signal is superimposed on the DC bias voltage so that the plate voltage and current slide up and down the load line around the operating point.

Normally we choose an operating point so that, under all input signal conditions, the grid voltage remains below 0V. In addition, we want the amplifier to be as linear as possible, so we operate in a region where the characteristic curves are evenly spaced.

In this example, a grid voltage of -1.0V to -1.5V seems reasonable, so we choose -1.1V, represented by point C. Other operating points may be as good or better.

The operating point determines several important amplifier parameters. First, the y-coordinate of point C is the *quiescent* plate current, in this example, 1.1mA. Quiescent circuit conditions are with no input signal. The x-coordinate of point C is the quiescent plate voltage, in this example, 150V. Note that we can also calculate the voltage drop across $R_L$ to determine the quiescent plate voltage. If $R_L$ is 100k ohms and $I_P$ is 1.1mA, the voltage drop across $R_L$ is 110V and the plate voltage is 260V – 110V, or 150V. Similarly, we can calculate the plate current from the plate voltage.

Since we now know the plate voltage and plate current, we can calculate the power dissipated by the plate (V X I), which is 165mW. The maximum allowable plate dissipation (from the 12AX7A specification) is 1.2W, so we are well within the limit under these conditions.

Finally, we can use the load line to calculate the gain of the amplifier. We can also see that at a grid voltage of -0.5V, the plate voltage is 110V, and at a grid voltage of -1.5V, the plate voltage is 175V. Therefore, when the grid voltage changes by 1V (1.5V – 0.5V) the plate voltage changes by 65V (175V – 110V). The gain is thus 65, or 36dB.

In order for the circuit in Figure 2.1 to operate properly, we need two DC supply voltages, a large positive voltage connected to the plate resistor and a small negative voltage connected to the grid. Alternatively, we can apply a positive voltage to the cathode and reference the grid to ground, resulting in the same negative grid-to-cathode voltage. We can do this with a single supply voltage, using a technique known as *cathode biasing.*

In Figure 2.3, we add two resistors to the circuit of Figure 2.1. $R_I$ is connected from the grid to ground, and $R_K$ is connected from the cathode to ground.

$R_I$ should be small enough to effectively tie the grid to ground, yet large enough to provide adequate input impedance.

**Figure 2.3** Cathode-biased Triode Amplifier

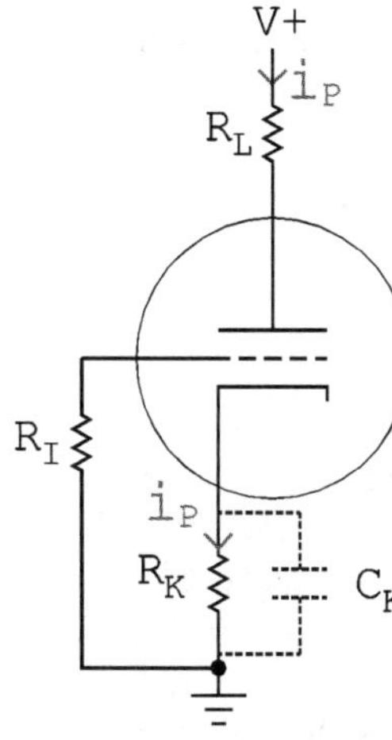


Because under normal operating conditions, negligible current flows in the grid, all of the plate current flows through $R_K$ to ground. Using the example above, if the desired grid-to-cathode voltage is -1.1V, we want the cathode voltage $V_C$ to be 1.1V. Since the quiescent plate current $I_P$ is 1.1mA, we choose $R_K$ as:

$$R_K = \frac{V_C}{I_P} = \frac{1.1V}{0.0011A} = 1000\Omega$$ **Equation 2.1.**

As we increase the grid voltage, the grid-to-cathode voltage increases, the plate current increases, and thus the cathode voltage also increases. This in turn decreases the grid-to-cathode voltage, resulting in negative feedback. Negative feedback reduces gain and distortion and improves stability. Another way to describe the effect of adding cathode resistance is that the cathode resistor effectively increases the plate resistance $r_p$ by $R_K(1+\mu)$, where $\mu$ is the amplification factor described in Chapter 1.

However, we may want the highest gain possible, and higher distortion may be acceptable or even desirable. To reduce the negative feedback associated with cathode biasing, we make the cathode an AC ground by attaching a large-value capacitor $C_K$ in parallel with $R_K$, as shown in Figure 2.3. AC current then flows through $C_K$ rather than $R_K$, so AC signals do not increase the cathode voltage. Thus, there is no negative feedback for AC signals. However, the DC voltage across $R_K$ remains constant, maintaining the bias condition. We will discuss the use of cathode bypass capacitors in greater detail later in this chapter.

As we have seen, once the tube has been chosen the performance of the amplifier depends on the supply voltage, the load resistor, and the choice of operating point. All are interdependent, so if you change one the others will also change. The effects of varying supply voltage, load resistance, and operating point are:

— **Increasing supply voltage:** All tubes have a specified maximum plate voltage, which you should not exceed. If you use a higher supply voltage, the maximum output voltage will be higher. Higher supply voltage will also cause more power to dissipate in the tube, so you should make sure that the maximum dissipation does not exceed the specified value. Line CD on Figure 2.4 shows the location of the load line if the supply voltage is raised to 310V and the load resistor remains 100kΩ. The output voltage can vary from around 100V to 310V, for a maximum swing of 210V. Looking at line AB, you can see that with a supply voltage of 260V the output voltage can vary from around 80V to 260V, for a maximum swing of 180V.

— **Decreasing supply voltage:** Amplifiers with lower supply voltages will begin distorting at lower output voltage levels, and their gain will be slightly lower with the same load resistor. Line EF on Figure 2.4 shows the location of the load line if the supply voltage is lowered to 210V and the load resistor remains 100kΩ. The lines for the various grid voltages are not as parallel and evenly spaced as they are on line AB, resulting in more distortion at high signal levels. They are also closer together, resulting in less gain.

— **Increasing load resistance:** If the load resistance increases, the gain, maximum output voltage swing, and output impedance increase. Line AG on Figure 2.4 shows the load line if the supply voltage is 260V and the load resistor is increased to 200kΩ. The load line is flatter, so the output voltage will vary more for a given change in grid voltage, resulting in higher gain. The lowest possible plate voltage is around 45V, 35V lower than the lowest possible plate voltage on load line AB, resulting in a higher maximum output voltage swing. The output impedance is the plate resistance of the tube in parallel with the load resistor, so increasing the load resistor will increase the output impedance slightly.

— **Decreasing load resistance:** If the load resistance decreases, the gain, maximum output voltage swing, and output impedance decrease. The load line is steeper, so the output voltage will vary less for a given change in grid voltage, resulting in lower gain. Line AH on Figure 2.4 shows the load line if the supply voltage is 260V and the load resistor is decreased to 65kΩ. The lowest possible plate voltage is around 110V, 30V higher than the lowest possible plate voltage on load line AB, resulting in lower maximum output voltage swing. The output impedance is lower because the load resistor is smaller.

— **Operating point:** In most cases the quiescent grid voltage should be about halfway between the 0V characteristic curve and the curve crossing the load line closest to the x-axis. This choice results in positive and negative output voltage peaks distorting at close to the same voltage, allowing the highest undistorted peak output voltage. However, in some cases you may want to intentionally cause either the negative or positive peak to distort first, in which case the operating point can be moved closer to the x-axis, resulting in distortion of positive waveform peaks first, or closer to the y-axis, resulting in distortion of negative waveform peaks first. Distortion will be discussed further in Chapter 3.

In most designs, supply voltage, load resistance, and operating point are chosen together to provide the desired load line and operating characteristics.

**Figure 2.4** Effect of Varying Supply Voltage and Load Resistance

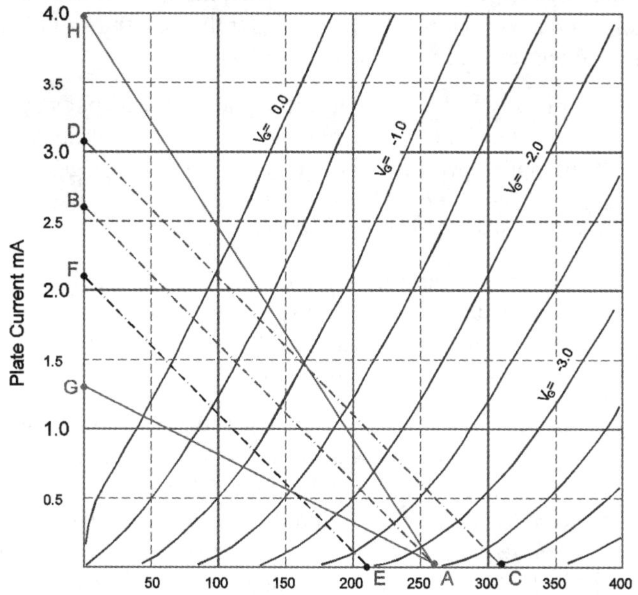


## Amplifier Block Diagram

Figure 2.5 shows the block diagram of a basic guitar amplifier with one channel and no effects or other added features. We discuss each block in detail in later sections.

**Figure 2.5** Basic Amplifier Block Diagram

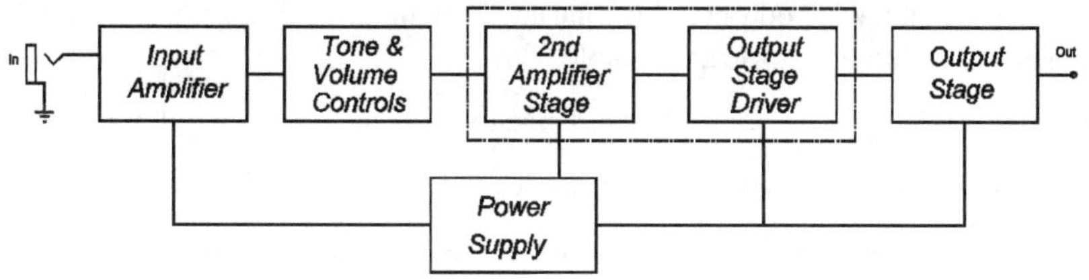


Overall, the amplifier takes a low-voltage, low-current input signal and converts it to higher-voltage, high-current output signal. It also shapes the signal's frequency response. We can distribute these functions throughout the amplifier stages in various ways.

In the basic amplifier of Figure 2.5, the signal goes through five stages from the guitar input to the speaker output:

1. The input amplifier, which boosts the signal level, provides a high input impedance to the guitar signal, and provides a relatively low output impedance to drive the tone and volume controls.
2. The tone and volume controls, which modify the signal's frequency response and level. This stage is usually implemented with passive devices (resistors and capacitors), which reduce the signal level somewhat and present design challenges with respect to input and output impedance.
3. A second amplifier stage, which provides additional gain. Together, the input amplifier and second amplifier stage provide most of the amplifier's voltage gain. The high input impedance of this stage provides a suitable load for the tone and volume controls. The first three stages are often referred to as the *preamplifier*.
4. The output stage driver, which conditions the signal for the output stage. Some simple amplifiers, such as the Fender Champ, combine the second amplifier stage with the output stage driver. Other, more powerful amplifiers require separate stages. In push-pull amplifiers, the output stage driver not only increases the signal level, it also produces two out-of-phase signals, one for each half of the output stage.
5. The output stage, which includes the output tubes and the output transformer. The output tubes convert the high-voltage, low-current signal from the output stage driver to a high-voltage, higher-current signal. The output transformer converts this signal to a lower-voltage, high-current output at the speaker terminals.

The power supply feeds DC voltages to all of the stages, except for the passive tone and volume control stage. The power supply is a voltage source, designed to provide fixed voltages at whatever current each stage requires. In general, the output stage requires the most current, and the preamplifier stages the least. Stages that amplify low-voltage, low-current signals, especially the input stage, require more elaborate power supply design to ensure low hum and noise. Stages that handle high-voltage or high-current signals, such as the output stage, can usually tolerate "dirtier" power, that is, DC voltages with more hum and noise. We will see how to design a power supply later in this chapter.

## Input Amplifier

The design goals of the input amplifier are:

- To handle any possible input signal level and provide a high input impedance.
- To amplify the signal for output to the tone and volume control stage, while adding as little unwanted distortion and noise as possible.
- To provide a relatively low output impedance to drive the tone and volume control stage.

We can achieve the first two goals fairly easily, while the third goal is more difficult.

Now, let's design an input amplifier. We first select the tube. There are many good choices, but we use the 12AX7A, the most common preamplifier tube.

Next, we choose a supply voltage. The specified maximum plate voltage for the 12AX7A is 330V, so we normally choose a supply voltage of 330V or less. Since the maximum peak-to-peak output voltage is slightly less than the supply voltage, we normally choose a plate voltage close to the maximum. The supply voltage also affects the load line and operating point.

Apart from ensuring that we don't exceed the maximum voltage, our choice of supply voltage depends on the power supply design and on the desired load line and operating point.

In theory, we can use a load resistor of any value, but in practice the possible range is more restricted. Several factors must be balanced when we choose the load resistor. First, the higher the load resistor the higher the gain. However, too high a load resistor will result in very low plate current, placing the load line at the bottom of the characteristic curves chart, where distortion will be high due to the non-linearity of the curves in that region. Further, stages with higher gain can have poor high-frequency response. We will discuss the reason for this later in this section. Too low a load resistor results in high plate current, which can cause plate power dissipation to exceed its specified limit.

As a general rule of thumb, the load resistor should be a minimum of 1.5 times the plate resistance, and a maximum of around one quarter of the input impedance of the following stage. The plate resistance of the 12AX7A is 62.5kΩ, which means the minimum load resistor value should be around 100kΩ. If the stage is feeding another amplifier stage with an input impedance of 1MΩ, our rule of thumb limits the maximum value of the load resistor to 250kΩ.

You can determine the optimal design for a particular stage by first designing the stage as we have discussed and then building the stage and listening to it with real signals, both alone and together with other stages of the amplifier being designed.

The frequency response of each stage, and of the complete amplifier, should be wide enough to amplify all frequencies present in the input signal without introducing unwanted changes in the response. The lowest fundamental frequency in a guitar signal (assuming standard tuning) is 82Hz, although guitar signals can include frequencies lower than 82Hz from picking or plucking the strings. The highest fundamental frequency is around 1.8kHz. Allowing for several harmonics, high frequency content from the pick attack, and additional high frequency energy from effects such as reverberation, the highest frequency of interest is still less than 10kHz. As we will see, this range of frequencies is fairly easy to amplify.

We will now discuss in detail the design of the input amplifier of Figure 2.6, including the plate circuit, the cathode circuit, and the grid circuit.

**Figure 2.6** Input Amplifier Circuit

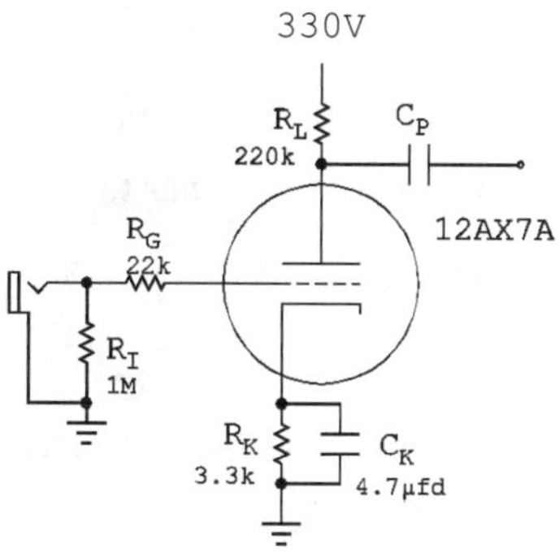

## Plate Circuit

For this example we have chosen a supply voltage of 330V and a load resistor of 220kΩ. Using these values we can construct the load line AB in Figure 2.7.

**Figure 2.7** Example Circuit Operating Parameters

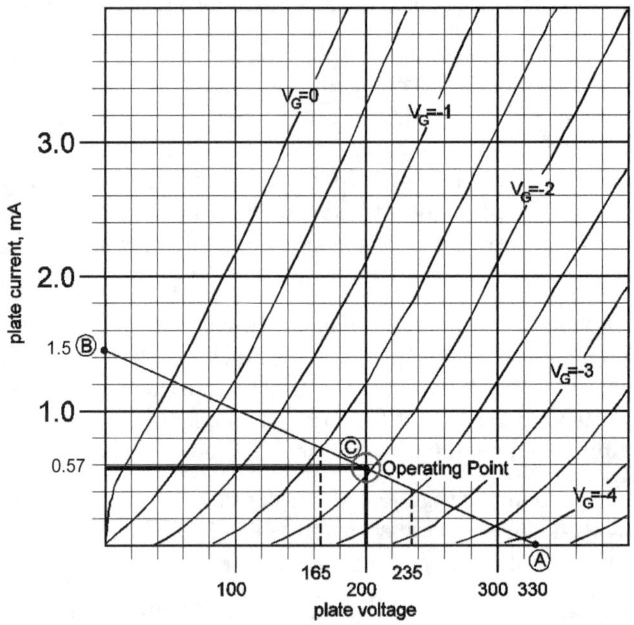


We choose the operating point C corresponding to $V_G$ = -2.0V. You can see that where the load line crosses the characteristic curve corresponding to $V_G$ = -2.5V the curve is not linear. This causes distortion at higher input signal levels, as the positive half of the signal waveform is amplified differently from the negative half. As $V_G$ varies from – 1.5V to – 2.5V, the plate voltage varies from 165V to 235V, so the gain is 70, or 37dB.

Capacitor $C_p$ is called the *coupling* capacitor. It blocks DC voltage from the plate while allowing AC signals to pass to the next stage. $C_p$ must be large enough to allow all frequencies of interest to pass. If $C_p$ is too small, low frequencies will be attenuated. However, because the input amplifier feeds the tone and volume control circuit, which provides its own coupling, we will not use a coupling capacitor in this stage. We will discuss coupling capacitors further in later sections of this chapter.

### *Cathode Circuit*

Referring to Figure 2.7, our operating point corresponds to a quiescent plate current of 0.57mA. The cathode resistor value is then $\frac{2V}{0.00057A}$, or 3.5kΩ. We will use 3.3kΩ, a close standard value.

Cathode bypass capacitor $C_K$ will introduce low-frequency attenuation and should be chosen to be large enough so that the low frequency attenuation begins well below the lowest frequency of interest. As explained in Chapter 1, the -3dB point for $R_K$ = 3.3kΩ and $C_K$ = 4.7μfd is:

$$f = \frac{1}{2\Pi R_K C_K} = 10Hz$$ **Equation 2.2**

The lowest frequency produced by a guitar (low E) is around 82Hz, so this is well below the range of interest. In actual practice the –3dB frequency is somewhat higher than calculated by Equation 2.2, and depends on the gain. Furthermore, all low frequency attenuation introduced in the amplifier will add, so it is best to choose a low frequency cutoff point sufficiently low to ensure that the amplifier's overall low frequency performance will not be affected.

In some amplifiers the cathode bypass capacitor value is intentionally reduced to shape the frequency response by attenuating lower frequencies. One famous example is the Marshall "Plexi," where one channel uses an 820Ω cathode resistor with a 250μfd bypass capacitor and the other channel uses a 2.7kΩ cathode resistor with a 0.68μfd bypass capacitor. The first channel has a calculated -3dB point of around 1Hz, while the second (bright) channel has a -3dB point of around 87Hz. Both of these frequencies are actually higher as noted above. Many players connect a jumper cable from one channel of the Plexi to the other to allow mixing the two signals to achieve a good tone.

## *Grid Circuit*

The maximum output voltage from a humbucking pickup is on the order of 1-2V peak-to-peak. Single-coil pickups have slightly lower output. Since the gain of our input amplifier is 70, the AC plate voltage with the maximum input signal is as high as 140V peak-to-peak. The supply voltage is 330V, and the quiescent DC voltage at the plate (from Figure 2.6) is 200V, so the amplifier can output over 200V peak-to-peak, and thus will handle the maximum output voltage swing with some room to spare.

Our input amplifier has a single input, which is connected to ground via $R_I$, a 1MΩ resistor. As explained in Chapter 1, under normal operating conditions negligible current flows into the grid, so the input impedance of the amplifier is defined by the input resistor, and thus in this case is 1MΩ.

In addition to very high impedance, the grid also exhibits capacitance. Since the grid, plate, and cathode are all made of metal, they act as small capacitors. The amount of effective capacitance depends on the gain, but is usually around 100pf. This capacitance acts together with the source resistance to form a low-pass filter.

$R_G$ is called the *grid-stop* resistor, and works together with the input capacitance to stabilize the amplifier by providing attenuation at very high frequencies. If we assume an input capacitance of 100pf, the –3dB point will be at 72kHz, using Equation 2.2. So, only frequencies above the audio range will be attenuated. All grid circuits must include grid-stop resistors.

Many guitar amplifiers have more than one input. Usually, they are arranged so that the gain from one is higher than the other. Figure 2.8 shows a typical two-input arrangement, used in many Fender amplifiers. Switched input jacks are used, where, if a plug is inserted, the switch contact, represented by an arrow in Figure 2.8, opens. If a guitar is plugged into input 2, the two 68kΩ resistors are placed in parallel by the input 1 switch, so the input resistor is 1MΩ and the grid stop resistor is 34kΩ. If a guitar is plugged into input 1, the 1MΩ resistor is connected to ground by the input 2 switch, so the input resistor is 68kΩ and the grid stop resistor is 68kΩ, attenuating the input signal by 6dB. If guitars are connected to both inputs, the input resistance is 1MΩ (slightly higher for input 1), and each input is routed through a 68kΩ resistor to the grid. These resistors allow the two signals to mix while minimizing interaction and also serving as grid stop resistors.

**Figure 2.8** Typical Fender Grid Circuit

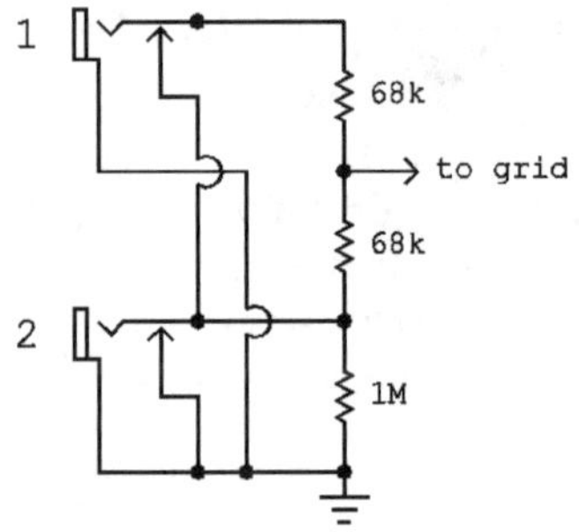


## Tone and Volume Control Circuit

Guitar amplifiers provide control of tone and volume using variable resistors, or *potentiometers*. As shown in Figure 2.9, potentiometers have three terminals, one each to the two ends of the resistive element and a third to the *wiper*, which you can move along the resistive element. The position of the wiper determines the resistance from the wiper to each end of the element.

**Figure 2.9** Potentiometer Schematic Symbol

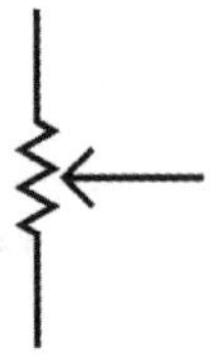

The resistive element can be linear, in which case moving the wiper a fixed distance always results in the same change in resistance, or logarithmic (sometimes referred to as *audio*), in which case moving the wiper a fixed distance results in an exponential change in resistance (for example, dB). This property is often referred to as the potentiometer's *taper*. Guitar amplifiers use both types. Volume controls use a logarithmic taper, while tone and other controls can be either linear or logarithmic, depending on the circuit and the desired response. Logarithmic taper potentiometers are often marked with an *A*, and linear tapers potentiometers with a *B*.

We can add a volume control to the input amplifier of Figure 2.6 as shown in Figure 2.10. In this application we use a logarithmic taper potentiometer, so changing the setting of the control by a fixed amount corresponds roughly to a fixed increase in volume.

The output impedance of the amplifier is equal to $R_L$ in parallel with the plate resistance of the tube. For the 12AX7A used, the plate resistance is 62.5kΩ, so the output impedance is 48kΩ. The value of the potentiometer should be large with respect to the output impedance, so we have chosen a value of 1MΩ. 500kΩ would also work well in this application. You can add $C_B$ to boost high frequencies. The amount of high frequency boost depends on the setting of the volume control, with more boost as the volume is reduced. The value of $C_B$ is usually on the order of 500pf.

Note that the choice of potentiometer value also depends on the following stage. In this example we assume that the next stage is another amplifier, with high input impedance, so the potentiometer also acts as the input resistor for the next stage, saving one resistor. This arrangement is used in many low-power, low-cost amplifiers, including early versions of the Fender Champ.

Now let's add a simple tone control, as shown in Figure 2.11. This circuit was used in the Magnatone M7 amplifier.

At low frequencies the impedance of the .0022ufd capacitor is high, so it has little effect on low-frequency signals. However, $R_1$ and $R_2$ form a voltage divider, so low frequencies are attenuated by 6dB. In general, if you want the tone control circuit to provide boost as well as cut, the circuit must attenuate the signal by approximately the amount of boost desired. So, if you want the tone controls to offer up to 10dB of boost, the circuit will attenuate the signal around 10dB. This loss is made up in the following stage.

**Figure 2.10** Input Amplifier with Volume Control

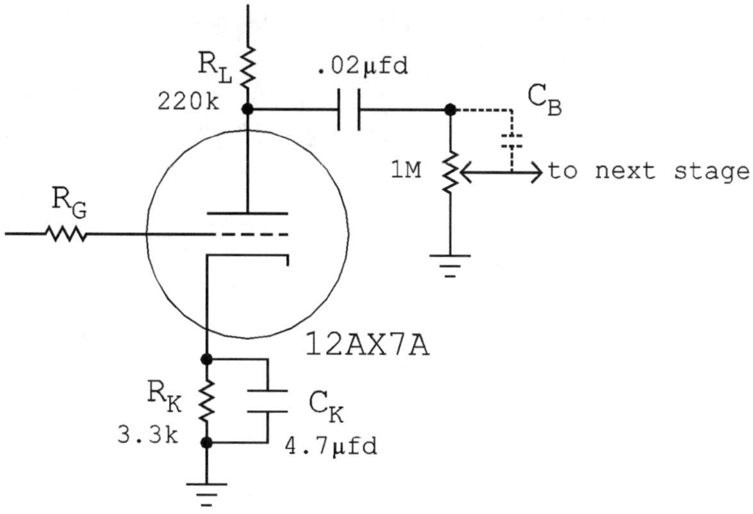


**Figure 2.11** Input Circuit with Volume and Tone Controls

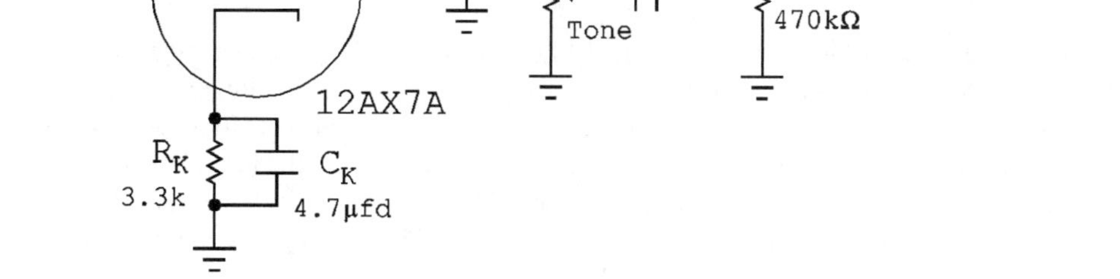


To understand what happens at higher frequencies, let's consider two situations: one when the potentiometer wiper is at the top of its range, so the .0022ufd capacitor is in parallel with $R_1$, and the other where the wiper is at the bottom of its range, so the .0022ufd capacitor is in parallel with $R_2$ (one end is grounded).

In the first situation high frequencies are boosted, because the .0022ufd capacitor's impedance lowers the parallel combination of $R_1$ and the .0022ufd capacitor, decreasing the attenuation of the voltage divider. At 154Hz, when the impedance of the .0022ufd capacitor equals $R_1$, the response is boosted by about 2.5dB, and the boost increases up to 6dB as frequency increases.

In the second situation high frequencies are attenuated, because the .0022ufd capacitor's impedance lowers the parallel combination of $R_2$ and the .0022ufd capacitor, increasing the attenuation of the voltage divider. Since $R_2$ equals $R_1$, the attenuation begins around the same frequency (154Hz), and increases as the frequency increases. Unlike the boost, the cut is not limited to 6dB. You can see the frequency response of this circuit with the tone potentiometer at mid-point and at both extremes in Figure 2.12.

**Figure 2.12** Response of Tone Control Circuit of Figure 2.11

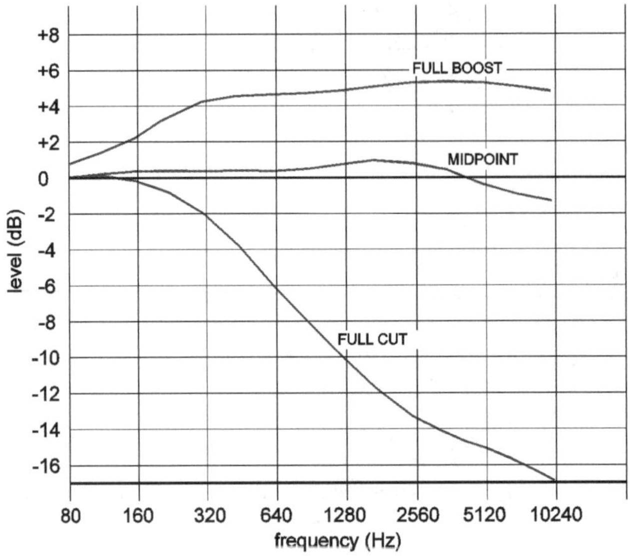


As the potentiometer is moved between the two extremes, the boost or cut varies between the two limits described above. Note that if we change the value of the .0022ufd capacitor it changes the frequency at which the boost or cut occurs. Lowering the value of the .0022ufd capacitor will raise the frequency and raising the value of the .0022ufd capacitor will lower the frequency. However, we have little reason to raise the .0022ufd capacitor's value, since the cut-off frequency is already quite low.

The input impedance of the circuit of Figure 2.11, viewed from the plate, depends on the setting of the volume and tone controls. We can consider the .02ufd coupling capacitor to be a short circuit at audio frequencies of interest. If the volume control is all the way down, the input impedance is 1MΩ. If the volume control is all the way up, the input impedance at low frequencies is the volume control resistance (1MΩ) in parallel with the tone control resistance (1MΩ) in parallel with $R_1$ and $R_2$ in series, or 333kΩ. At high frequencies the .0022ufd capacitor acts in parallel with $R_1$, $R_2$, or both, depending on the setting of the tone control. The combined impedance of the three components will approach 470kΩ. The resulting input impedance is 1MΩ in parallel with 1MΩ in parallel with 470kΩ, or about 240kΩ. In all cases the input impedance is relatively high with respect to the tube's output impedance.

The output impedance is less important, due to the high load impedance of the following stage. The output impedance also depends on the settings of the volume and tone controls, and at low frequencies will be 235-280kΩ. At high frequencies the output impedance can be much lower, depending on the setting of the tone control.

In this design, the relatively high value of $R_1$ (470kΩ) together with the input capacitance of the next stage can cause high frequency roll-off.

If we want separate bass and treble controls, we can add the classic Fender tone control circuit to our input amplifier, as in Figure 2.13.

**Figure 2.13** Input Amplifier with Volume, Bass, and Treble Circuit

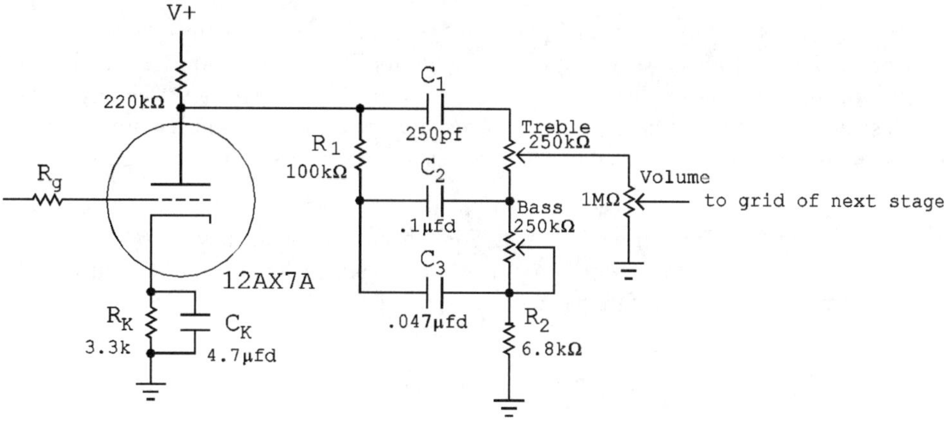


The operation of this circuit is harder to understand, as we now have three capacitors, two potentiometers, and two resistors to consider. Also, the volume control has been moved from the input of the tone control circuit to the output. This provides a high load impedance for the tone control circuit and a suitable input resistor for the next stage. The source impedance is the output impedance of the input amplifier, or 48kΩ.

Consider the circuit at high frequencies. First, $C_2$ and $C_3$ will have relatively low impedance at high frequencies, so they can be thought of as short circuits, simplifying the circuit to the one shown in Figure 2.14.

**Figure 2.14** Equivalent Circuit for Figure 2.13 at High Frequencies

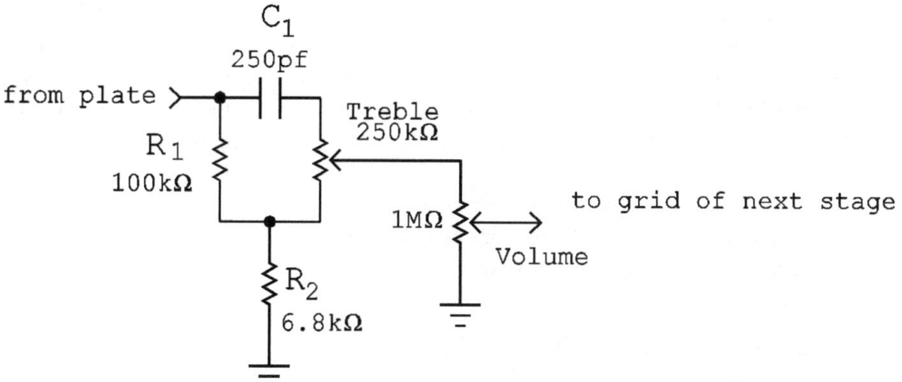


Because the value of $R_2$ is low with respect to $R_1$ and the treble control, it can also be considered a short circuit, so $C_1$ and the treble control in parallel with the volume control form a first-order high-pass filter with a cut-off frequency at around 3kHz. As we noted previously, changing the value of $C_1$ changes the cut-off frequency. $R_1$ forms an attenuator with the output impedance of the input amplifier and $R_2$, causing a reduction in signal level of about 3.5dB and allowing some full-range signal to pass to the bottom of the treble control.

If the wiper of the treble control is at the top of the potentiometer, high frequency signals pass to the volume control and the next stage. If the wiper is at the bottom of the potentiometer, high frequencies are attenuated, due to the voltage divider created by $R_2$ and the treble control. If the wiper is in the middle, high frequency signals are attenuated around 12dB. So, we can think of this circuit as a treble control that introduces around 15dB of attenuation and provides 12dB of boost or cut above 3kHz, with progressively less boost or cut at frequencies below cut-off.

At low frequencies the impedance of $C_1$ becomes very high, and $C_1$ can be thought of as an open circuit. Figure 2.15 shows the equivalent circuit for Figure 2.13 at low frequencies. First, note that the setting of the treble control affects the low frequency signal level slightly, because the resistance of the treble control forms a voltage divider with the volume control. However, the maximum difference between the two extremes of the wiper is only around 2dB.

If the wiper of the bass control is at the top of the potentiometer, the control is shorted and $C_2$ and $C_3$ are in parallel. They form a HPF with $R_2$ with a cut-off frequency of 160Hz. But, $R_1$ and the output impedance of the input amplifier form a voltage divider with $R_2$, causing 27dB of attenuation above the cut-off frequency and more below. So, in this position the low frequency signals are attenuated.

**Figure 2.15** Equivalent Circuit for Figure 2.13 at Low Frequencies

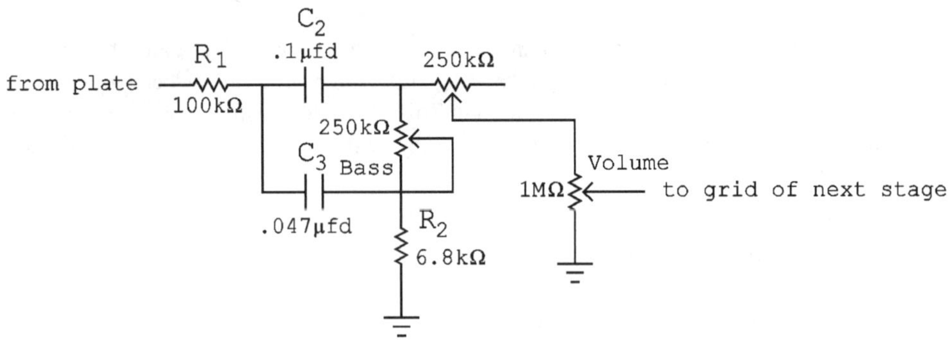


If the wiper of the bass control is at the bottom of the potentiometer, $C_2$ forms a HPF with the bass control in series with $R_2$, with a cut-off frequency of about 6Hz. More importantly, the voltage divider formed by $R_1$ and the bass control in series with $R_2$ now introduces only about 3dB of attenuation, so low frequency signals are passed to the bottom of the treble potentiometer and on to the next stage. High frequencies are passed by $C_3$ to the junction of $R_2$ and the bass control, causing them to be attenuated by 24dB starting at a cut-off frequency of around 500Hz. So, we can think of this circuit as a bass control that introduces around 15dB of attenuation and provides around 12dB of boost or cut at low frequencies, with the amount of boost or cut gradually reducing as frequencies rise to about 500Hz. Changing the value of $C_3$ affects the upper frequency limit of the control.

Frequency response curves for the tone control circuit of Figure 2.13 are shown in Figure 2.16.

As you can see, the treble control has an effective range of about 20dB, with more boost available than cut. The bass control has an effective range of about 14dB at 80Hz, with more cut available than boost. You can also see a broad dip in the midrange (sometimes referred to as *scoop*), especially evident in the curve with bass and treble controls set at 5. Note that this dip remains even with bass and treble set to 10, although it is at a lower frequency.

**Figure 2.16** Response of Tone Control Circuit of Figure 2.13

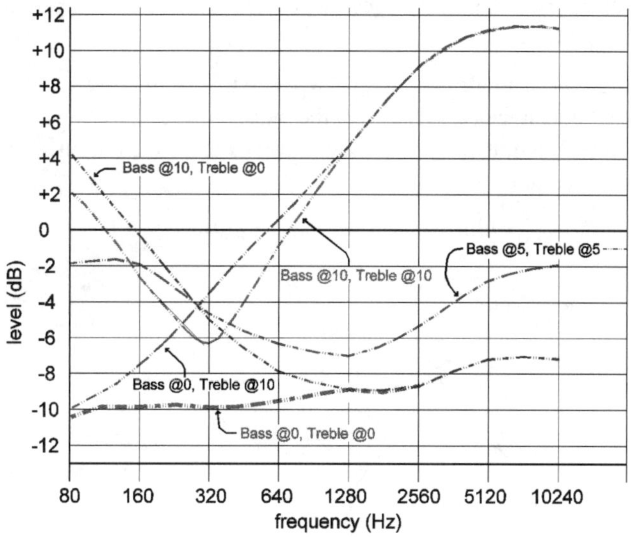


The input impedance of this circuit varies with frequency and the setting of the controls. At low frequencies the minimum input impedance is $R_1$ plus $R_2$, since $C_1$ can be thought of as an open circuit. As noted earlier, this causes low frequency signals to be attenuated by a few dB. At high frequencies we can consider $C_1$ in Figure 2.14 to be shorted, so, if we neglect the effect of the volume control, the input impedance is $R_1$ in parallel with the treble control, plus $R_2$, or 78kΩ. Thus, high frequency signals are also attenuated somewhat.

The output impedance of the tone control circuit depends on the settings of the bass and treble controls. However, it will always be comfortably below the load resistance of 1MΩ (the resistance of the volume control).

We can draw several conclusions from our analysis of the volume and tone control circuit of Figure 2.13:

— The frequency response with the tone controls set to their midpoints is not flat. This is referred to as the *voicing* of the amplifier, an important artistic consideration. We choose the amplifier's voicing to provide the best sound when it is used to amplify a guitar signal.

— The boost and cut characteristics are not symmetrical. They are chosen to provide a range of control for obtaining useful sounds with a variety of guitars.

— The controls interact. For example, in Figure 2.16 you can see from the Bass@10, Treble@10 and Bass@10, Treble@0 curves that the bass signals decrease in level when the treble control is turned up.

— Tone control circuits that provide boost cause overall signal loss. The amount of loss depends on the circuit, but in all cases this loss must be made up by later amplifier stages.

We can design tone control circuits that do not interact and that provide flat overall response. However, this is often not the best sounding approach, and to implement such circuits requires additional components and amplifier stages.

## Second Amplifier Stage

The second stage provides additional gain to recover losses from the tone and volume control circuit and provide sufficient signal level to drive the next stage. In addition, it *buffers* the tone and volume control circuit from later stages by providing high input impedance and comparatively low output impedance.

Most small amplifiers use a single output tube. We call this *single-ended* (SE) operation. In this configuration, the second stage usually drives the output tube directly. In more powerful amplifiers with push-pull (PP) output stages, the second stage feeds the output stage driver, which is discussed in the next section.

**Figure 2.17** Second Amplifier Stage

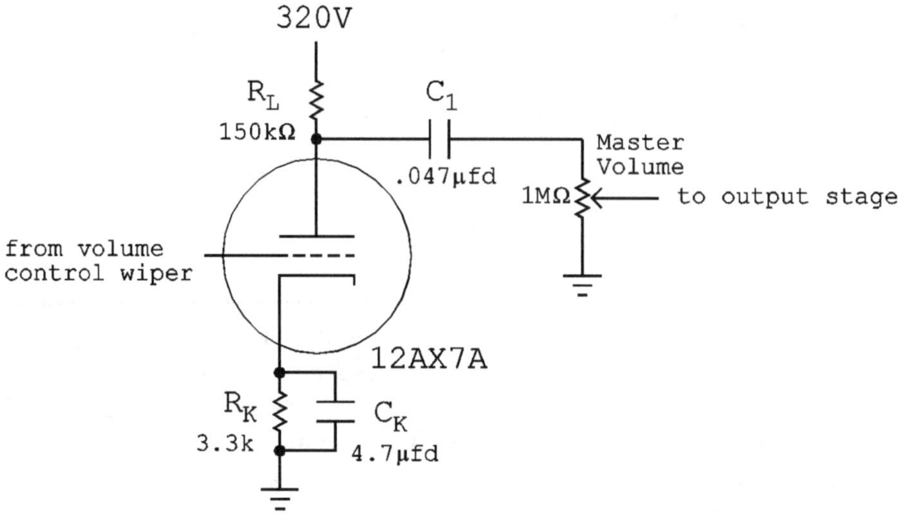


Figure 2.17 shows a typical second stage circuit. The design is similar to the input amplifier of Figure 2.6, but the load resistor value has been reduced to 150kΩ. We can see the effect of this change by looking at the load line in Figure 2.18.

As the grid voltage varies from -1.5V to -2.5V, the plate voltage varies from 180 to 245V, so the gain is 65, or 36dB. This is slightly less than the gain of the input amplifier of Figure 2.6, and the operating point is in a location where large signals are amplified more linearly.

Since the input amplifier has a gain of 37dB, the tone control circuit has a loss of around 20dB with the tone controls at midpoint, and the second amplifier stage has a gain of 36dB, we now have up to 53dB of gain available, depending on where the volume control is set. Given a 2V peak-to-peak output from the pickup, the output voltage from the second stage with the volume control all the way up is over 500V peak-to-peak, clearly impossible with a 320V plate supply voltage. So, we know that the second amplifier stage distorts under these conditions. If the bass or the treble control is adjusted higher than midpoint, the distortion occurs at a lower input level at the boosted frequencies.

**Figure 2.18** Load Line for Amplifier Stage of Figure 2.17

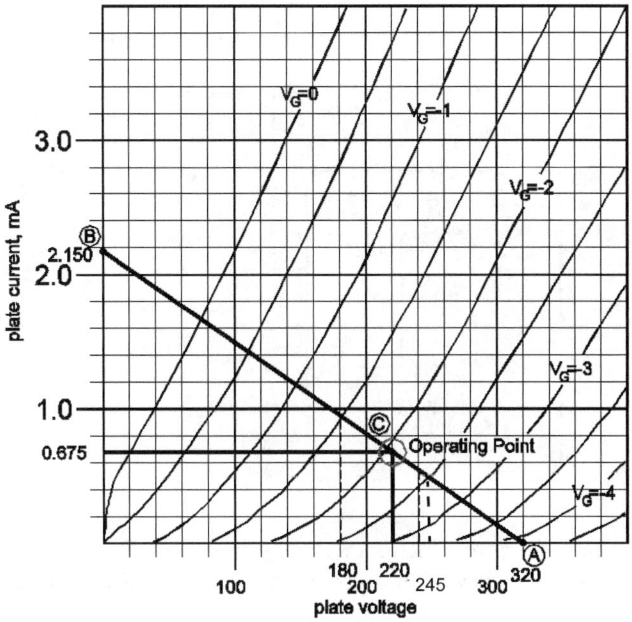


## Output Stage Driver

In many low-power single-ended amplifiers the output of the second amplifier stage is adequate to drive the output tube. Higher-power push-pull amplifiers require two out-of-phase signals to drive the output stage. We also often need to provide additional gain to drive the output stage to full power.

In this section we discuss two circuits that provide out-of-phase (or *differential*) outputs from a single-phase input. This process is usually referred to as *phase splitting*. There are several other phase splitter designs, but the two discussed below are the ones most commonly used in guitar amplifiers.

### *Cathodyne Phase Splitter*

The cathodyne phase splitter is also called the *concertina* phase splitter. A single stage is used to provide both phases. Many well-known guitar amplifiers use a cathodyne splitter, including the Ampeg Gemini and Reverberocket amplifiers and the later Fender Princetons. An additional gain stage is usually placed before the cathodyne phase splitter. To understand how the cathodyne circuit works, we must first discuss a new circuit called a *cathode follower*.

You can see in Figure 2.19 that a cathode follower is simply the amplifier stage of Figure 2.3 with the load resistor moved from the plate to the cathode. We also move the output to the cathode, with $C_2$ blocking the DC voltage while allowing AC signals to pass.

**Figure 2.19** Cathode Follower Circuit

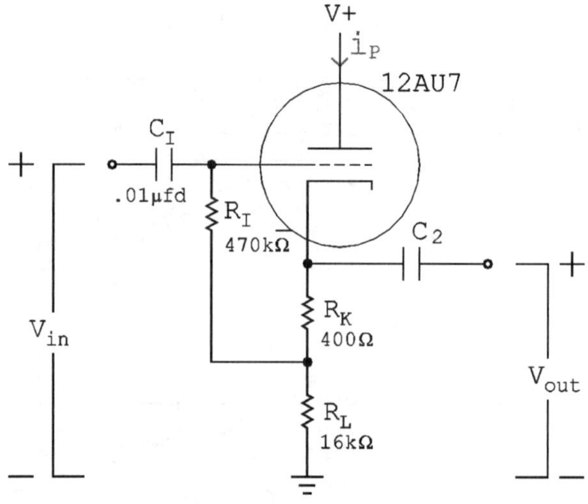


Since the plate and cathode current increases as the grid voltage increases, the voltage at the cathode also increases due to the voltage drop across $R_K$ plus $R_L$. So, the voltage at the cathode is in phase with and "follows" the grid voltage.

Resistors $R_K$ and $R_I$ bias the grid in exactly the same way as in the amplifier of Figure 2.3. Because the value of $R_L$ is usually around twice the plate resistance, the DC voltages at the cathode and the grid are high. $C_1$ blocks the DC voltage at the grid from the circuit feeding the cathode follower while allowing AC signals to pass. Note that the output can also be taken from the junction of $R_K$ and $R_L$, which improves the stability of the circuit at the expense of a slight decrease in output.

Because the voltage at the cathode follows the grid voltage, the circuit provides no voltage gain. In fact, cathode followers generally have a gain of slightly less than one. This property provides 100% internal negative feedback, resulting in very low distortion.

Even though they do not provide voltage gain, cathode followers have other useful properties. First, they exhibit very high input impedance. Because the voltage at the cathode follows the voltage at the grid, the voltage across $R_I$ is quite low and the current flowing through $R_I$ is much lower than if $R_I$ were grounded. The resulting input impedance is usually five to ten times higher than the value of $R_I$.

Second, the input capacitance is much lower than in a plate-loaded amplifier stage. This is because of the internal negative feedback mentioned above and the fact that the plate is held at a constant voltage. The input capacitance of a cathode follower is so low it can generally be ignored in audio-frequency applications such as guitar amplifiers.

Finally, while cathode followers do not provide voltage gain, they can amplify current. The output impedance of a cathode follower is the inverse of the transconductance, usually less than 1kΩ, so they can drive relatively low-impedance loads. This combination of high input impedance and low output impedance makes cathode followers ideal for use as buffers to prevent interactions between stages of an amplifier.

Cathode followers are designed using the same techniques used for the input and second stage amplifiers. However, because cathode followers are used to amplify current, we need to use a tube that has high current sourcing capability. The 12AU7A is a good choice.

Using the characteristic curves for the 12AU7A and assuming a plate voltage of 320V and a load resistance of 16kΩ, we draw the load line and choose the operating point as shown in Figure 2.20. The operating point chosen corresponds to a grid voltage of -4V with respect to the cathode and a plate current of 10mA. Therefore, $R_K$ must be $\frac{4V}{10mA}$, or 400Ω. The maximum allowable value for $R_I$ from the 12AU7A data sheet is 1MΩ, but, as explained earlier, we can use a lower value while still assuring high input impedance, so we choose 470kΩ. A lower input resistance reduces noise generated by the stage. We choose the values of $C_1$ and $C_2$ to ensure that low frequencies are not excessively attenuated. The choice of $C_1$ is somewhat arbitrary, but a value around .01ufd is probably a good choice. The value of $C_2$ will depend on the load impedance.

The DC voltages at the cathode and grid are much higher in a cathode follower than in a plate-loaded amplifier stage. Again referring to Figure 2.20, you can see that the operating point corresponds to a DC voltage of 168V. By subtracting this value from the plate voltage (320V), we find the cathode voltage, in this case 152V. The grid voltage is then 148V. When designing cathode followers you must be careful to ensure that the maximum voltage difference between the cathode and the heater does not exceed the specified value for the tube used. For a 12AU7A, the specification is 180V, so the heater supply voltage can be close to ground without harming the tube.

**Figure 2.20** Characteristic Curves for Cathode Follower Circuit of Figure 2.19

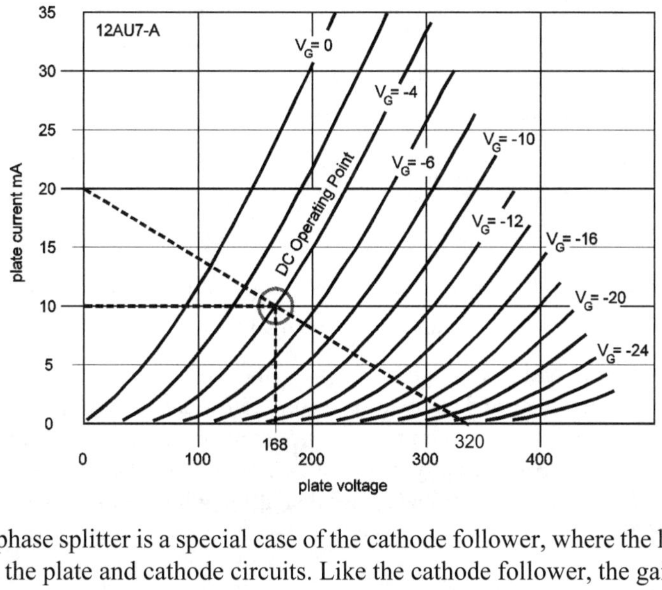


The cathodyne phase splitter is a special case of the cathode follower, where the load resistance is split between the plate and cathode circuits. Like the cathode follower, the gain is slightly less than one but current is amplified. The same criteria also apply to the tube used, so we again use the 12AU7A in this example.

Referring to Figure 2.21, you can see that $R_{L1}$ is connected to the plate circuit and $R_{L2}$ is connected to the cathode circuit, with positive and negative outputs taken from the cathode and plate, respectively. The same current flows through $R_{L1}$ and $R_{L2}$, so, assuming they are the same value, the AC voltages at the cathode and plate are essentially the same level with opposite phase.

We choose the load resistance in exactly the same way we did for the cathode follower circuit of Figure 2.19, except we divide the total resistance in half and use 8kΩ for $R_{L1}$ and $R_{L2}$.

We then choose a grid bias voltage that results in DC voltages at the plate and cathode that provide the largest possible voltage swings before distortion. Because the two signal voltages are out of phase, we need DC voltages at the cathode equal to one quarter of the supply voltage and at the plate equal to three-quarters of the supply voltage. The voltage at the plate will then vary between the supply voltage and one-half the supply voltage, and the voltage at the cathode will vary between one-half the supply voltage and ground. With our 320V supply voltage, we want the quiescent DC voltage at the plate to be 240V and at the cathode 80V. That in turn means we want the quiescent bias current to be 10mA to drop 80V across 8kΩ. Referring to Figure 2.20, we see that a grid bias voltage of -4V results in 10mA of plate current, so once again the proper value for $R_K$ is 400Ω.

**Figure 2.21** Cathodyne Phase Splitter

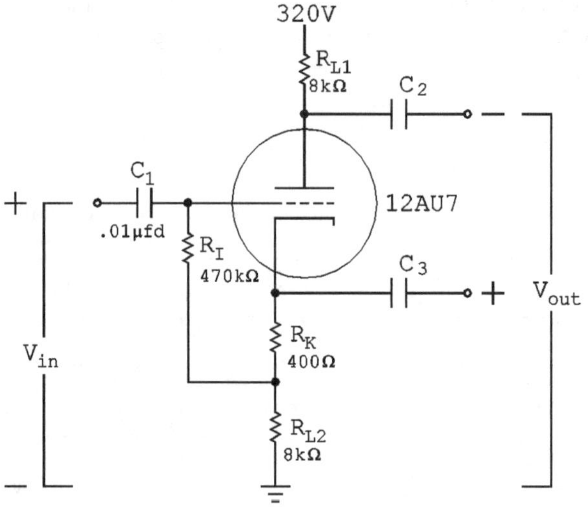


$C_1$ and $R_I$ can remain the same as in Figure 2.19, and $C_2$ and $C_3$ should again be chosen to provide adequate low frequency performance for the load impedance being driven.

The input impedance is again a multiple of $R_I$ due to the internal negative feedback. The output impedances differ at the plate and cathode. The output impedance at the plate is approximately $R_{L1}$, or 8kΩ in our example. The output impedance at the cathode will be much lower due to the internal negative feedback, usually less than 1kΩ as discussed earlier. This difference in output impedance can cause level imbalances when driving load impedances that are different and when overdriving the stage.

## *Long-Tail Pair Phase Splitter*

Differential amplifiers, as the name implies, amplify the difference between two signals. They are used in a wide variety of applications, including microphone preamplifiers and, in a different configuration, phase splitters.

All differential amplifiers have two inputs, and the output voltage is defined as:

$$V_O = A \times (V_1 - V_2), \quad \textbf{Equation 2.3}$$

where $V_O$ is the output voltage, A is the gain, $V_1$ is the input voltage to one terminal and $V_2$ is the input voltage to the other terminal. $V_1$ and $V_2$ are often the same signal, but out of phase. When the two signals are subtracted by the differential amplifier, any noise that appears on both signals is cancelled, while the signal itself is doubled. The result is excellent noise performance, so differential amplifiers are often used in difficult applications such as in noisy environments and with very low signal levels.

You can see from Equation 2.3 that if either $V_1$ or $V_2$ is zero, the output voltage is just the gain of the amplifier times the other signal. With $V_2$, the signal is inverted as well. So, differential amplifiers can be driven by a single or *unbalanced* signal. The output of a differential amplifier can be either unbalanced, with one output signal, or *balanced*, with two identical but out-of-phase signals.

There are many ways to implement differential amplifiers. We will discuss one such implementation, known as the *long-tail pair* or *Schmitt* circuit. The long-tail pair has balanced inputs and outputs, and is used in many guitar amplifiers, including most high-power Fenders and Marshalls.

The basic long-tail pair circuit is shown in Figure 2.22. The cathodes of the two tube sections are connected together to a current source I, so $I_1 + I_2 = I$. We can implement the current source in a number of ways, most of which require an additional tube. The simplest solution is to connect a large value resistor between the cathode and ground, which tends to keep the total current constant by providing internal feedback.

**Figure 2.22** Basic Long-Tail Pair Differential Amplifier

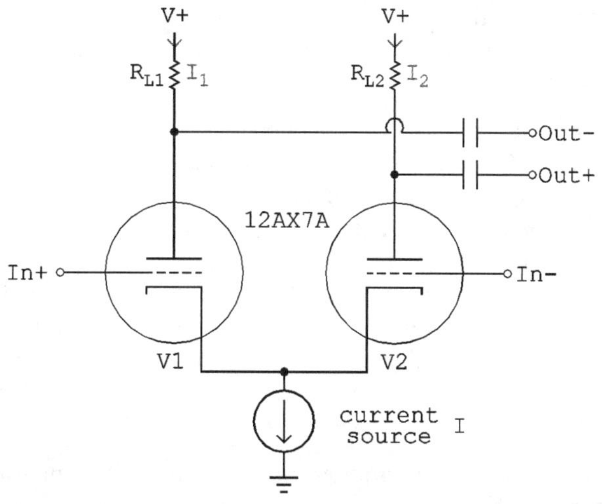


If the current through one tube rises, the current through the other tube falls by the same amount. Thus, the two outputs are always equal and out of phase. If the signal at the + input rises, the voltage at the plate of $V_1$ falls and the voltage at the plate of $V_2$ rises. Similarly, if the voltage at the – input rises, the voltage at the plate of $V_2$ falls and the voltage at the plate of $V_1$ rises. Either or both of the inputs and outputs can be used. In our phase splitter, we use one input and both outputs.

A typical long-tail pair phase splitter circuit is shown in Figure 2.23. For now, ignore $C_3$ and $R_7$ and assume that $C_2$ is connected to ground. The circuit has two outputs, taken from the plates of $V_1$ and $V_2$, and one input, at the grid of $V_1$. The grid of $V_2$ is tied to ground through $C_2$, which allows it to be biased to the proper DC voltage while shunting AC signals to ground.

**Figure 2.23** Long-Tail Pair Phase Splitter Circuit

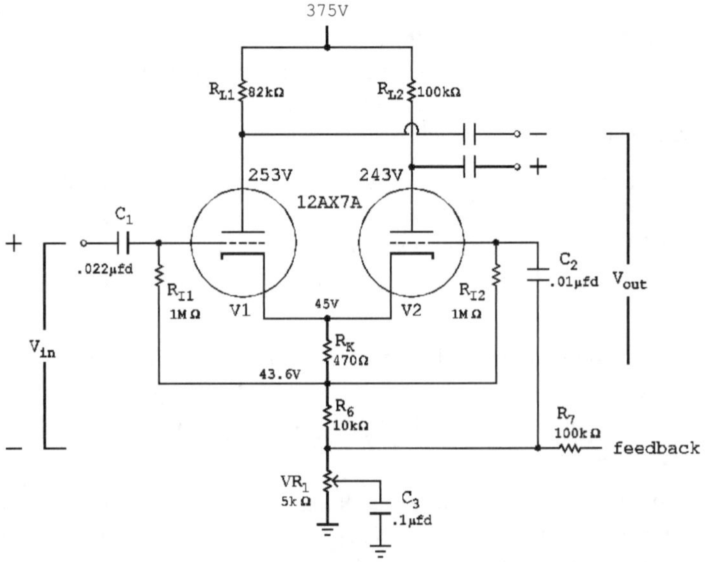


The grids are biased in the usual manner, with input resistors $R_{I1}$ and $R_{I2}$ and cathode resistor $R_K$. When choosing the value of $R_K$, remember that the bias voltage generated is the result of plate current from both $V_1$ and $V_2$. The input impedance is higher than the value of $R_{I1}$ due to the internal negative feedback generated by $R_6$, as in the cathode follower circuit discussed earlier. As also mentioned earlier, the values of $C_1$ and $C_2$ should be just large enough to prevent unwanted low-frequency roll-off. Some designers specify a value for $C_2$ 10 times the value of $C_1$, for example, .01ufd for $C_1$ and 0.1ufd for $C_2$.

You select load resistors $R_{L1}$ and $R_{L2}$ and the operating point using the characteristic curves and load line described earlier. However, the cathode current will cause a significant voltage drop across $R_6$, and this voltage must be subtracted from the power supply voltage to determine the total voltage across the tube. In this circuit the DC voltage at the cathode will be around 45V, so we use an effective supply voltage of 330V to create the load lines. The load lines and operating points are shown in Figure 2.24. You make $R_{L1}$ lower than $R_{L2}$ to balance the two output voltages, since the gains of the two stages are slightly different. However, you may want the stage to be slightly unbalanced to generate certain output stage distortion. Also, if the tail resistor is larger than around 15kΩ, the balance may be better using equal-value resistors for $R_{L1}$ and $R_{L2}$.

From Figure 2.24 you can see that the grids are biased about -1.4V with respect to the cathode, and the quiescent currents in $V_1$ and $V_2$ are about 1.5mA and 1.3mA respectively. The total cathode current is 2.8mA, so the voltage at the cathode is almost 44V. The quiescent voltages at the plates of $V_1$ and $V_2$, after adding the DC voltage at the cathode, are 249V and 241V respectively.

The DC voltage at each plate can be as high as the plate supply voltage, 375V, or as low as the cathode voltage plus the plate-to-cathode voltage, around 100V. So, the AC voltage swing at the plates can be as much as 250V peak-to-peak before the stage begins to distort.

The voltage at the plate of $V_1$ varies from 226V to 286V as the grid voltage varies from -1V to -2V, so the gain of that section is 60, or 35.6dB. The voltage at the plate of $V_2$ varies from 214V to 279V under the same conditions for a gain of 65, or 36.3dB.

**Figure 2.24** Load lines for Phase Inverter of Figure 2.23

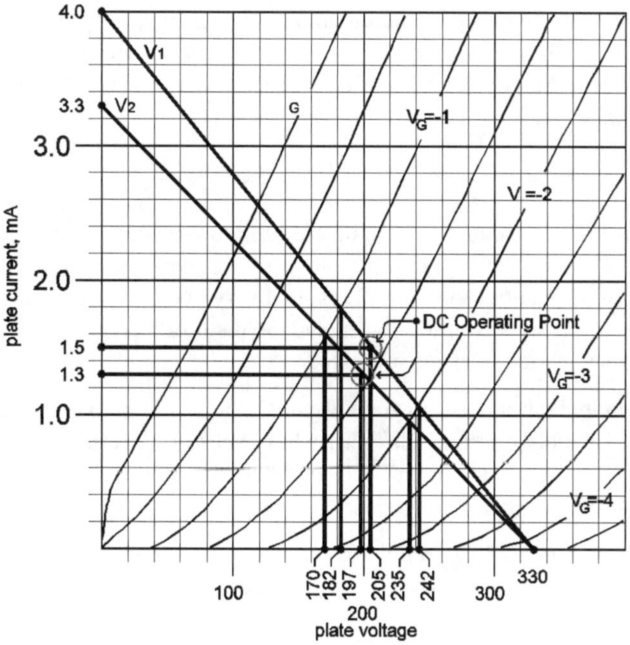


The value we choose for $R_6$, the *tail* resistor, is a compromise. On the one hand, we want to provide a large output voltage swing, which calls for a lower value of $R_6$ to keep the DC voltage at the cathode as low as possible. On the other, higher values of $R_6$ provide a more constant cathode current, improving balance and linearity. In general, you should use the highest value possible given the supply voltage and operating point used. Typical values range from 6.8kΩ to 24kΩ. Power dissipation in the tubes must also be kept within specified limits, which is of concern when high supply voltages and plate currents are used.

In many circuits negative feedback is applied from the speaker output to the phase splitter. Negative feedback reduces distortion and lowers the output impedance of the amplifier. It also, as already noted, increases the input impedance and reduces the gain. The feedback signal is routed through $R_7$, which forms a voltage divider with $VR_1$. The ratio of $R_7$ to $VR_1$ determines the amount of negative feedback applied.

The signal is then fed to the negative input of the phase splitter via $C_2$. This signal is subtracted from the phase splitter's input signal, thus providing negative feedback. The feedback signal is also applied to the cathode circuit at the junction of $R_6$ and $VR_1$. This signal changes the cathode current, which causes both the plate voltages to vary in phase. So, it adds to one output and subtracts from the other, depending on the phase of the feedback signal. The gain of this signal is much lower than the gain provided from the positive and negative inputs, so its effect will be relatively minor. It is used to correct imbalance in the gains of the two sections from the feedback input. We will discuss negative feedback more in the next section.

We can implement a presence control by using a potentiometer as the shunt element in the feedback voltage divider and attaching a capacitor to its wiper. $C_3$ shunts high frequencies from the feedback signal to ground, thereby reducing the amount of negative feedback and increasing the gain of the stage at high frequencies. Because the amplifier's output impedance is affected, it also sounds "looser" at these frequencies. The higher the value of $C_3$, the lower the frequencies that are affected by the presence control.

## Output Stage

This section discusses the two most common output stage designs, single-ended and push-pull. In addition, we describe how output stages are biased and the *classes* of biasing, a commonly-misunderstood concept. Finally, we discuss how to select the proper output transformer for a particular output stage.

### Single-ended Output Stage

Single-ended output stages are most commonly used in low-power amplifiers, often because they cost the least. They are generally the simplest designs, which make them ideal for starting our discussion of output stages. They can also sound very good, as long as high output power is not needed. Low-level signals sound sweet, and the distortion created by an over-driven single-ended output stage is rich in even harmonics.

The single-ended output circuit, as shown in Figure 2.25, is similar to the basic amplifier circuit of Figure 2.3. The only difference is that we have substituted a transformer for the load resistor. We are also using a pentode tube. Triode output tubes do exist, but are not commonly used in guitar amplifiers.

**Figure 2.25** Single-ended Pentode Output Stage

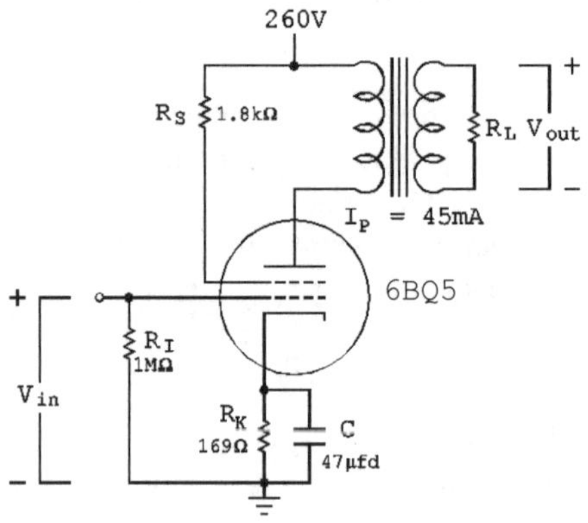


As described earlier, the suppressor grid is tied to the cathode, often internally, so it is not shown in Figure 2.25. The screen grid is tied to the power supply through grid-stop resistor $R_S$. This makes the plate current virtually independent of the plate voltage, as we will see later in this section. Some current, usually around 10% of the plate current, flows in the screen grid circuit, so the cathode current does not exactly equal the plate current in a pentode. However, the difference is relatively minor and can often be ignored when designing pentode output stages. The screen grid can also be used in other ways, but tying it to a fixed DC voltage is the normal practice in guitar amplifiers.

The primary winding of the transformer has low resistance, so the quiescent voltage at the plate is essentially equal to the power supply voltage. When an AC signal is applied to the grid, the plate current and transformer primary current vary and cause current to flow in the transformer secondary winding and $R_L$. Interestingly, the voltage at the plate is higher than the supply voltage on positive-going waveforms, due to the energy stored as magnetic flux in the transformer. With signal present, the average plate current is constant and equal to the quiescent current, since the higher currents on positive waveform peaks are balanced by the lower currents on negative peaks.

The maximum peak power output of a single-ended stage is equal to the maximum rated power dissipation for the tube used. The average power output is thus one-half the maximum rated dissipation. In order to achieve maximum power output, the quiescent plate current is chosen so that the plate power dissipation is at or near the specified maximum. The average power dissipation with signals present is about the same.

We choose the output transformer primary impedance to provide the maximum rated power output with the given supply voltage. For the 6BQ5 tube used in Figure 2.25, the maximum plate dissipation is rated as 12 watts, so with a power supply voltage of 260V the quiescent plate current should be $\frac{12W}{260V} = 46mA$. Using Ohm's law we can calculate:

$$Z = \frac{V}{I} = \frac{260V}{0.046A} = 5.7k\Omega$$ . **Equation 2.4**

Remembering that the impedance ratio of a transformer is the square of the turns ratio, an 8Ω secondary load requires a turns ratio of about 27:1 to obtain a primary impedance of 5.7kΩ. A 4Ω load requires a turns ratio of 38:1, and a 16Ω load requires a turns ratio of 19:1.

We can now plot load line A in the normal way, as shown in Figure 2.26. However, only the slope of load line A is correct. Its proper position is defined by the plate dissipation. You can see the "Plate Dissipation = 12W" curve in Figure 2.26. We move the load line so that the slope remains the same but the vertical position is at or near the maximum dissipation curve, as shown by load line B. Now we can select our operating point by finding the point on load line B corresponding to a plate voltage of 260V.

**Figure 2.26** 6BQ5 Characteristic Curves with Load Lines

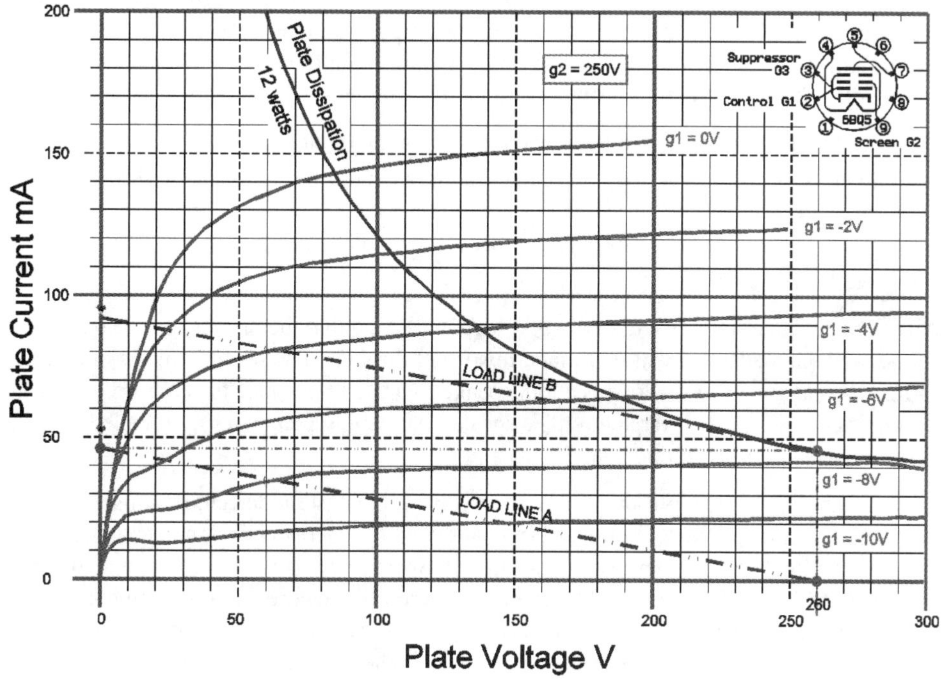

Cathode resistor $R_K$ is chosen so that the quiescent current times $R_K$ equals the grid voltage corresponding to the operating point. Referring to Figure 2.26, you can see that the operating point corresponds to a grid voltage of about -7.8V with respect to the cathode. Therefore, $R_K$ should be $\frac{7.8V}{0.046A} = 169\Omega$. $C_K$ is chosen to increase the gain by reducing internal feedback at audio frequencies. The value chosen (47ufd) will result in 3dB of low-frequency attenuation around 20Hz, well below the lowest frequency of interest.

The characteristic curves for the 6BQ5, a pentode, are quite different from the curves we saw previously for the 12AX7A and 12AU7A triodes. You can see that plate current is relatively independent of plate voltage, causing the curves to be flat. This is due to the screen grid, which is kept at a constant DC voltage and thus maintains a constant flow of electrons from the cathode when the plate voltage varies. You do this, as mentioned earlier, by connecting a fixed supply voltage to the screen grid through a grid stop resistor. The screen grid voltage must always be less than the quiescent plate voltage. The resistor should be at least 1kΩ, high enough to keep current and power dissipation in the screen grid circuit within specified limits. Excessive screen grid power dissipation is a common cause of output tube failure.

Note that the characteristic curves of Figure 2.26 specify a screen grid voltage of 250V. If a different screen grid voltage is used, the curves are different. In our case we have chosen a screen grid resistor of 1.8kΩ and the screen grid current is specified on the data sheet as 5.5mA, so, with a supply voltage of 260V, the screen grid resistor drops 10V and the voltage at the screen grid is 250V.

We can calculate the voltage gain of the stage from the characteristic curves. For example, in Figure 2.26, if the grid voltage changes from -6V to -8V, the plate voltage changes from 168V to 285V, so the gain is 58, or 35dB. Note, however, that this gain is measured at the primary of the output transformer. If the transformer secondary has an impedance of 8Ω, the turns ratio will be 27:1 (the square root of 5700/8). so the voltage gain to the secondary will be 58/27, or about 7dB. The current gain is, however, much higher.

Again referring to the tube specifications, we see that the input resistor $R_I$ must be 1MΩ or less when the tube is cathode biased, so we use that value in our design. As with the other stages, very little current flows in the grid under normal operating conditions, so the input impedance is basically equal to $R_I$. If the stage is overdriven, however, grid current flows, and this has an effect on the driver stage.

All of the design criteria discussed in this section assume that the primary of the output transformer and the load are resistive. In fact, this is not the case. The primary of the output transformer is inductive, and the load is a loudspeaker, whose impedance depends on the speaker, the enclosure design, and frequency. The speaker has a big effect on a single-ended amplifier's performance and the resulting sound.

Because single-ended amplifiers have a relatively high, constant current flowing through the output transformer primary, the core of the transformer is specially designed to avoid problems associated with the flux generated by the current. Specifically, an *air gap* is provided to reduce the flux in the core, thus avoiding magnetic saturation of the core and resulting distortion. Single-ended output transformers are generally larger, heavier, and more expensive than equivalent output transformers for push-pull output stages. They also generally have poorer high- and low-frequency response and lower efficiency. All of these issues are of more concern in hi-fi applications than in guitar amplifiers, where more limited frequency response is acceptable and non-linearity is often desirable.

If more power is desired, output tubes can be operated in parallel, as shown in Figure 2.27. The design is developed in the same way, except currents are multiplied by the number of paralleled tubes, as is output power. As we shall see in the next section, however, there are other ways to more efficiently achieve similar results.

**Figure 2.27** Single-ended Output Stage with Paralleled Tubes

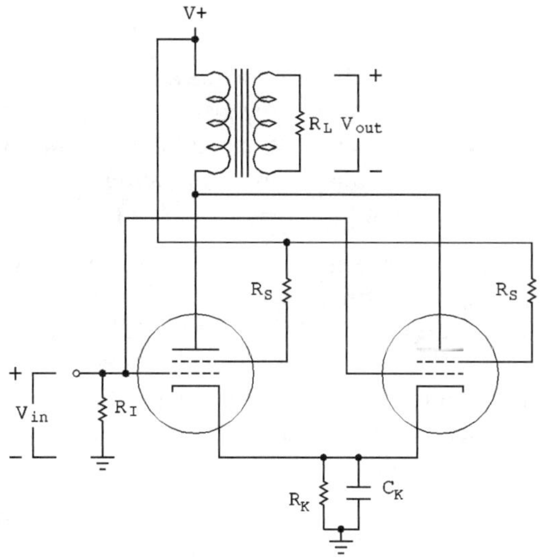


## *Push-pull Output Stage*

Push-pull output stages are used when higher power is desired. As shown in Figure 2.28, pairs of output tubes are driven out-of-phase, with their plates connected to each end of a center-tapped transformer. The output signal is the difference of the two input signals. The transformer's center tap is connected to the power supply.

This approach has several advantages. First, if the output tubes are balanced, the DC plate currents are equal but opposite and the net DC current in the primary of the output transformer is zero, resulting in no quiescent flux. This means you can use a smaller, lighter, cheaper transformer compared to a single-ended output stage. Second, any hum from the power supply that is present on the input signals will be cancelled, since the two input signals are subtracted. This relaxes the power supply design requirements.

**Figure 2.28** Basic Push-pull Output Stage Circuit

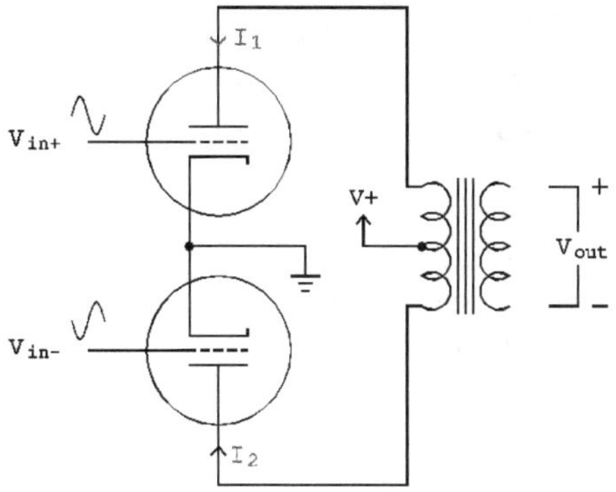

Third, you can shift the operating point of the output tubes to produce significantly more output power. You can do this because one side can amplify positive-going portions of the waveform while the other side amplifies negative-going portions. So, each tube operates part of the time, allowing more current to flow when the tube is conducting while maintaining average plate dissipation below the specified maximum.

## *Classes of Operation*

The operating point chosen determines the class of operation of the stage. In all of the examples we have discussed so far, current flows in the plate under all normal signal conditions. When no signal is present, there is quiescent DC current flowing. An AC signal at the grid causes this current to vary, but there is still always some current flowing. This is known as *class A* operation.

In *class B* operation the output tube is biased at cutoff, so there is no quiescent DC current. When the AC voltage on the grid is positive, current flows. When the AC voltage on the grid is negative, no current flows. So, the tube acts like a rectifier, allowing only half of the input waveform to pass. In theory, each side of a class B push-pull output stage amplifies one-half of the input, so the resulting output includes both halves. In practice, non-linear tube characteristics near cutoff and mismatched output tubes and transformer primary characteristics cause class B stages to have unacceptable distortion, so they are not used in audio applications.

However, elements of class A and class B can be combined to create output stages with higher efficiency than class A but acceptable distortion. This is known as *class AB* operation, where the operating point is above cutoff but still in an area where the tube cuts off during peaks of the negative-going waveform. Most push-pull output stages operate in class AB, due to its higher efficiency compared to class A. A range of operating points can be chosen for class AB operation, with resulting sonic differences. This is sometimes referred to as "hot" (closer to class A) or "cold" (closer to class B) biasing.

Class B and AB operation are illustrated in Figure 2.29.

**Figure 2.29** Class B and AB Operation

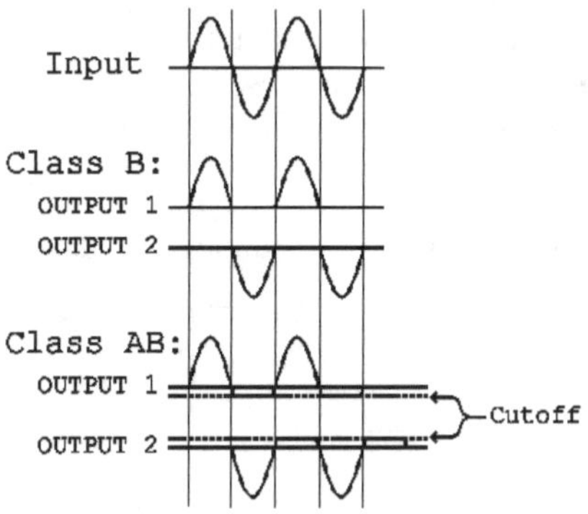


The signal at the top represents the input. In class B operation, the output of one tube in the push-pull stage would be as shown on the second line, while the output of the other tube would be as shown on the third line. You can see that in both cases the output occurs only during one-half of the signal cycle. The tube's cutoff voltage corresponds to the solid horizontal lines.

The fourth and fifth lines represent the two outputs in class AB operation. You can see that in this case some output occurs during both halves of the input signal's cycle, but during one half the output flattens when the input signal reaches the cutoff voltage. In these cases the cutoff voltage is represented by a dashed horizontal line in Figure 2.29. The two output signals overlap some, which decreases the distortion (aptly referred to as *crossover distortion*) caused when the signal crosses over from one tube to the other. The efficiency of the class AB stage is somewhat lower than a class B output stage, but still considerably higher than a class A stage.

## *Cathode vs. Fixed Biasing*

Up to this point we have used cathode biasing to establish the proper quiescent DC voltage at the grid. High-power output stages often use a different arrangement, where a separate negative DC voltage is generated in the power supply and applied to the grid, while the cathode is grounded. We will refer to this as *fixed* biasing.

The advantages of fixed biasing include:

— More power output for a given supply voltage. Since the cathode is grounded, the entire supply voltage is applied across the tube.

— Different individual tubes of the same type exhibit different plate currents with the same bias voltage due to normal variations in the manufacturing process. By allowing adjustment of the bias voltage, precise control of the quiescent current is possible. You can choose different quiescent bias currents, from class A to "hot" class AB to "cold" class AB, according to which sounds the best. When you replace the output tubes, you can set the quiescent current exactly as before.

The disadvantages of fixed biasing include:

— You must readjust the bias current when the tubes are replaced, and sometimes during the life of a set of tubes, due to changes in tube characteristics as they age.

— An additional supply voltage and other components are required, adding some complexity and expense.

— If the bias voltage increases due to a power supply failure or a short circuit, the bias current can increase catastrophically, damaging the tubes, the output transformer, or the power supply.

The advantages of cathode biasing include:

— No adjustments are needed when output tubes are replaced.

— Cathode-biasing is inherently self-regulating, since higher plate currents cause the voltage at the cathode to increase, making the grid more negative with respect to the cathode, which reduces the plate current. So, failures are less likely to damage components.

The disadvantages of cathode biasing include:

— You obtain less power output for a given supply voltage than with fixed biasing.

— Different tubes will draw different quiescent currents with a given cathode resistor, due to normal tube variations. So, when you change tubes your quiescent bias may also change, causing a change in performance.

Ultimately, your choice of fixed or cathode biasing should be made based on the power supply, the desired output power, and on which scheme sounds better.

## *Push-pull Output Stage Design*

A typical push-pull output stage is shown in Figure 2.30. We have again chosen to use the 6BQ5 tube with a 260V supply for this example.

The grid circuit includes $C_{I1}$ and $C_{I2}$, which connect to the outputs of the phase splitter. The value of $C_{I1}$ and $C_{I2}$, together with the output impedance of the phase splitter and the value chosen for $R_{I1}$ and $R_{I2}$, determines the low frequency response of the output stage. The 0.1ufd value shown in Figure 2.30 ensures adequate low frequency response when driven by the phase splitter circuit of Figure 2.23 and with $R_{I1}$ and $R_{I2}$ as shown. $R_{I1}$ and $R_{I2}$ are connected to the bias supply, which supplies the negative DC voltage necessary to bias the tubes properly, in this case around -7.5V. Referring to the 6BQ5 data sheet, the maximum allowable value for $R_{I1}$ and $R_{I2}$ in fixed-bias operation is 0.3MΩ, so our chosen value of 220kΩ is reasonable.

**Figure 2.30** Typical Push-pull Output Stage

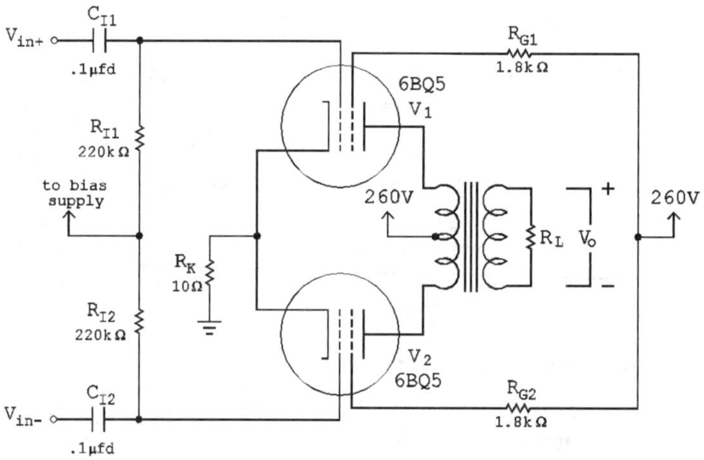


The two cathodes are connected to ground through resistor $R_K$. $R_K$ has a small value (in this case 10Ω) and is used to sense the current flowing through the cathodes to allow proper adjustment of the bias voltage feeding $R_{I1}$ and $R_{I2}$. For example, if we want a quiescent bias current of 30mA in each tube, a total of 60mA flows through $R_K$, resulting in a voltage drop across $R_K$ of 0.6V. By measuring the voltage across $R_K$, we can adjust the bias supply voltage for whatever quiescent current we want. You can also connect individual 10Ω resistors to each cathode. This allows you to measure the quiescent current through each tube independently. You should use matched output tubes to ensure that the currents through each tube are relatively equal, within 10-20% of each other. Note that the accuracy of the bias current adjustment will depend on the accuracy of the resistor(s), which should be 5% or better.

The screen grids are connected to the 260V supply through $R_{G1}$ and $R_{G2}$, as in our single-ended design, resulting in about 250V at the screen grids.

The plate circuit uses an output transformer with a center-tapped primary, with the center tap of the primary connected to the 260V supply. Each end of the primary is connected to a plate, so the current for $V_1$'s plate in Figure 2.30 flows from the center tap through the upper half of the primary, and the current for $V_2$'s plate flows from the center tap through the lower half of the primary. This arrangement is significant for several reasons:

— The two currents flow in opposite directions, so, assuming they are equal, no net DC current flows in the primary. This means there is no quiescent magnetic flux in the transformer, so all flux generated is the result of AC signals.

— None of the DC or AC current flowing to $V_1$ flows in the lower half of the primary, and none of the DC or AC current flowing to $V_2$ flows in the upper half of the primary. The two halves of the primary operate independently. You can easily see why this is true for DC current. For AC signals, the center tap acts as a *floating ground*, since the impedance of the power supply to AC signals is low. So, all AC current related to $V_1$ appears only in the upper half of the primary, and all AC current related to $V_2$ appears only in the lower half of the primary.

— In effect, half of the turns in the primary are connected to $V_1$, while the other half are connected to $V_2$. Since the impedance is proportional to the square of the turns ratio, this means that the primary impedance seen by $V_1$ and $V_2$ is one-fourth of the total primary impedance.

To determine the characteristics of a push-pull output stage, we arrange two sets of characteristic curves as shown in Figure 2.31. The curves are joined together with their current axes going in opposite directions to represent current flow in the two tubes. They are joined horizontally at the supply voltage, in this case 260V.

You choose the primary impedance to achieve the desired power output with the available supply voltage. The lower the primary impedance, the higher the power output for a given supply voltage. Under all circumstances, your choice should ensure that the load line as shown in Figure 2.31 is within the "plate dissipation = 12W" curves. For our design we have chosen a fairly conservative primary impedance of 8000Ω, so each plate will see an effective primary impedance of 2000Ω. You can see that the load line is well within the maximum dissipation limits, so we could choose a lower primary impedance, with resulting higher output power, if desired. To achieve maximum output power, draw the load line so that it just touches both maximum dissipation curves, then calculate its slope and use an output transformer whose primary impedance is four times the value calculated. In this design, you'd achieve maximum possible output power with a primary impedance of around 6000Ω. Operating output tubes at maximum rated plate dissipation will shorten tube life.

The first step is to draw a load line through the 260V point on the x-axis with a slope equal to the load impedance seen by each tube, in this case 2000Ω. You can do this using Ohm's law. For example, with a 2000Ω impedance, a change in current of 100mA corresponds to a change in voltage of 2000Ω x 100mA = 200V. This line represents the operating characteristics of the two tubes together. Current flows in each tube, with one tube providing the majority of the current at each end of the load line and both tubes contributing equally at the middle.

If we operate the grids so that the grid voltage never exceeds zero volts, the maximum peak-to-peak grid voltage will be 12V if the grid is biased at -6V. With 12V peak-to-peak at the grid, 115mA of current will flow in each tube on respective negative and positive signal peaks. Substituting equation 1.3 into equation 1.1, $W = I^2 \times R$ , so 115mA of current flowing through the 2000Ω primary will produce a peak power output of about 26W. As discussed previously, the average power will be one-half of this, or 13W. Since one tube provides $13W_{avg}$ of power for positive-going signals and the other provides $13W_{avg}$ of power for negative-going signals, the total output power will be $13W_{avg}$. There will be considerable distortion at the maximum output power, due to the non-linearity of the characteristic curve for 0V at the grid where it intersects the load line.

With the quiescent operating point at -6V, the stage is operating in class A at low signal levels and class B at the extremes. This is, as previously discussed, class AB operation. If we move the operating point lower, for example to -8V, the stage operates in class B more of the time and class A less. The allowable input voltage swing is higher, as is the peak output power, and distortion at low signal levels is higher. We can also move the operating point higher, even high enough to operate the stage in class A under all conditions. However, the allowable input voltage swing is lower and peak output power is also lower.

The class of operation in a push-pull output stage is determined by the choice of operating point and, as long as you don't exceed the maximum allowable plate dissipation, you can, as explained earlier, change from "cold" class AB to "hot" class AB to class A by simply adjusting the bias current for the appropriate operating point. More information on choosing an appropriate operating point can be found at the webervst site listed in the bibliography.

As with the SE amplifier, we calculate the voltage gain of the stage from the composite characteristic curves. For example, in Figure 2.31, if the grid voltage changes from -6V to -8V, the plate voltage changes from 140V to 180V, so the gain is 20, or 26dB. If the transformer secondary has an impedance of 8Ω, the turns ratio will be 16:1 (the square root of 2000/8), so the voltage gain to the secondary will be 20/16, or about 2dB.

If you need more power, output tubes can be operated in *parallel push-pull* configuration, similar to the topology shown in Figure 2.27.

**Figure 2.31** Characteristic Curves for 6BQ5 Push-pull Output Stage with 260V Plate Supply, 250V Screen Grid Supply

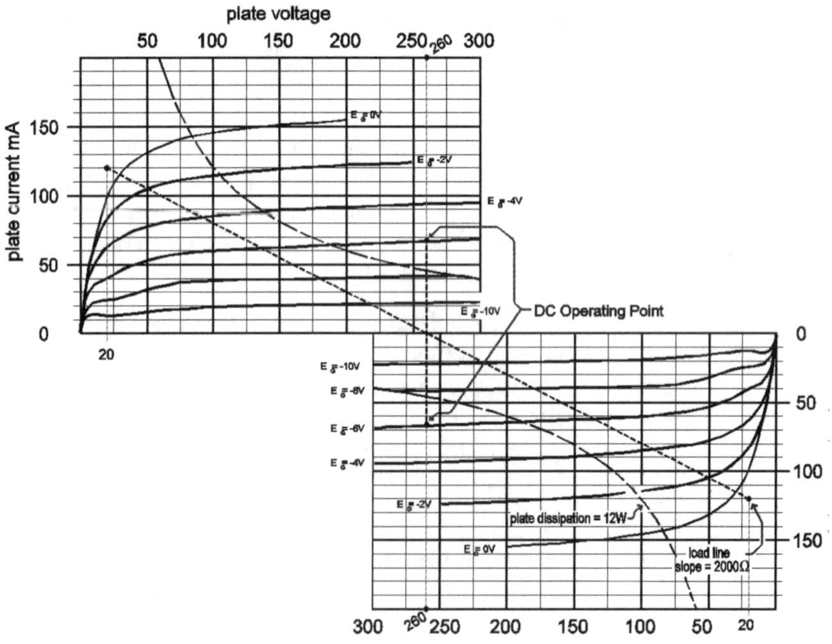


## *Feedback*

In many guitar amplifiers negative feedback is applied from the speaker output to the negative input of the phase splitter. As we discussed in the section on phase splitters, negative feedback reduces distortion, improves stability, and reduces the overall gain. It also lowers the output impedance and raises the input impedance. Figure 2.32 shows a typical output stage (the Fender Deluxe) with negative feedback.

**Figure 2.32** Output Stage with Negative Feedback

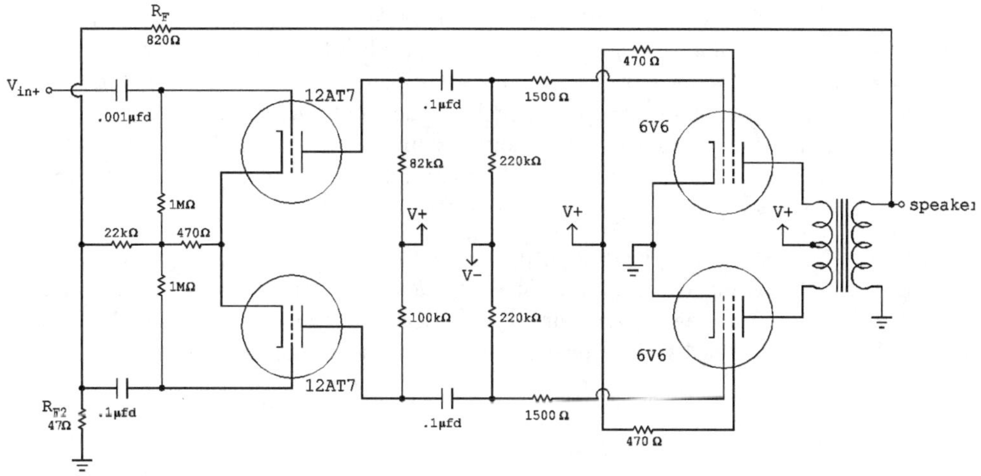


$R_F$ in Figure 2.32 forms a voltage divider with $R_{F2}$, and the resulting signal is fed to the minus input and the cathode circuit of the phase splitter. The amount of output signal that is fed back is called the *feedback fraction* (β), and determines the gain of the combined phase splitter and output stages. In Figure 2.32,

$$\beta = \frac{47}{820 + 47} = 0.054 \text{ . } \textbf{Equation 2.5}$$

As long as the gain of the stage without feedback is relatively high, the gain with feedback is:

$$A = \frac{1}{\beta} \text{ . } \textbf{Equation 2.6}$$

In the circuit of Figure 2.32, the gain is then $\frac{1}{0.054} = 18.5$, or about 25dB.

If the feedback network is purely resistive, as in Figure 2.32, the gain is generally independent of frequency, although phase shift in the output stage can affect gain at high frequencies. We can, however, make the feedback frequency-dependant, as with the presence control of Figure 2.23, where high frequency gain can be boosted with respect to low frequency gain. We can also boost the low frequencies by adding a capacitor in parallel with $R_F$. The frequency at which the boost begins is determined by the time constant of $R_F$ and the parallel capacitor.

You can determine the amount of gain reduction provided by the feedback network by calculating the total gain of the driver stage and the output stage and comparing that figure with A. The difference between the two figures is the amount of gain reduction due to the feedback. You can also measure the gain of the driver/output stage, then disconnect the feedback network and re-measure, and compare the two figures. Typically, feedback causes around 5-12 db of gain reduction.

## Signal Levels, Gain Staging and Headroom

When we connect the blocks together to form a complete amplifier, we must consider the input signal level, the gain, and the signal handling capability of each stage. If the input signal level is too high the stage distorts, and if the input signal level is too low the stage may be noisy. If the gain is too high the stage may also distort, while if the gain is too low there may be insufficient output to drive the next stage. While some distortion may be desirable, the characteristics of the distortion produced depend largely on the input signal level and the design of the stage. Given a defined input signal level and gain, the stage must be able to produce the desired output signal, whether it is an undistorted version of the input signal or has desired distortion characteristics.

In order to ensure that an amplifier design operates as intended, we must know the signal levels at key points in the circuit. We often use a level diagram to illustrate signal levels at various points in the circuit. A somewhat generalized level diagram is shown in Figure 2.33. Note the use of "dBV" on the vertical scale, referring to dB relative to a reference voltage of 1V.

**Figure 2.33** Typical Signal Level Diagram

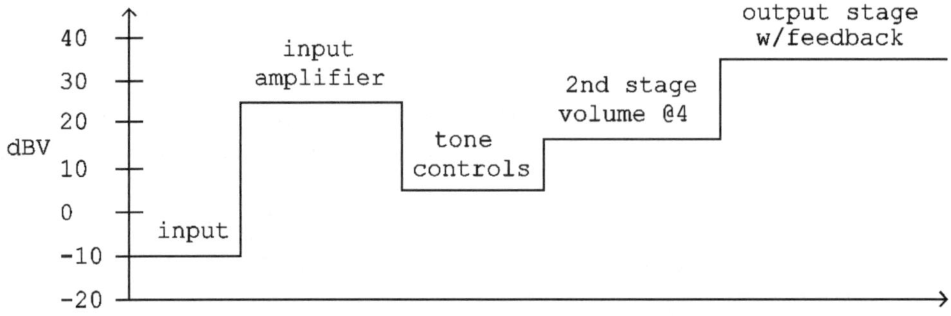


You can see that some stages (such as the amplifier stages) increase signal levels, while other stages (such as the tone controls) decrease signal levels. The signals handled and amount of gain provided by each stage must be carefully chosen to optimize performance of each stage and the overall amplifier. Again referring to Figure 2.33, you can see that the input amplifier stage provides 37dB of gain, after which the tone controls attenuate the signal by about 20dB. The precise amount of attenuation provided by the tone controls depends on frequency and the setting of the controls.

Absolute levels in the rest of the circuit are determined by the setting of the volume control. In Figure 2.33 we assume that the volume control is set 30dB below its maximum output level, so the second amplifier stage will provide 6dB of net amplification to the signal. Assuming the output stage has a gain of about 20dB, the output level, for an input signal level of -10dBV, is then 33dBV, or about 45V.

Levels at each stage of the amplifier should be kept as high as possible to maximize the ratio of signal to noise (the *signal-to-noise ratio, or SNR*). Usually, that means you want to amplify the input signal as much as possible as soon as possible, as the lowest-level signals are most likely to be affected by amplifier hum and noise.

However, each stage has limited signal handling capability. The maximum voltage that can pass undistorted depends largely on the power supply voltage and the design of the stage. Consider the signal illustrated in Figure 1.34. The DC component is 40V. Let's assume that the power supply voltage to this stage is 80V, so that the DC component is exactly one-half of the power supply voltage (which, as you will see, is a sensible choice). If the peak level of the negative half of the AC waveform in Figure 1.5 reaches -40V, the peak is at 0V and unable to go any more negative (since the lowest possible voltage is 0V). Likewise, if the positive half of the wave reaches 40V, it is equal to the 80V power supply voltage and unable to go any higher in voltage. If you increase the level further, the peaks of the wave flatten, causing distortion. Therefore, the maximum signal voltage that can be handled by this stage is 40V peak, or 28 $V_{rms}$. In actual practice, the signal handling capability of the stage is slightly less than $28V_{rms}$ due to various factors.

When you design an amplifier, the gain of each stage should be chosen to maintain the optimal relationship between signal level and overload characteristics. This does not necessarily mean that each stage overloads at the same signal level. For example, the first stage usually overloads at much higher levels due to the low input signal level; this is why many players boost their signal level before the amplifier input. Further, you may want to purposely overload certain stages (such as an overdrive channel) while other stages remain linear. Finally, the settings of the controls in the circuit affect overload characteristics.

However, you should make all such choices based on knowledge of the signal handling characteristics of each stage, the desire to maintain optimal SNR, and the intent to either avoid or create distortion in a given stage and in the entire amplifier. We will examine these choices further in Chapter 3.

## Power Supply

The last circuit block we will discuss in this chapter is the power supply. The power supply is arguably the most important part of the amplifier, and it has a big effect on the sound. Not only does the supply design affect hum and noise, it also affects the response of the amplifier. We often describe a power supply as "stiff" or "soft," and the same terms are used for the sound of the amplifier employing the supply. Furthermore, the supply is the most critical part of the amplifier in terms of safety and reliability.

As with all of the other blocks, many variations are possible. Guitar amplifiers normally use fairly simple power supply designs. The two circuits discussed are intended for use in a high-power amplifier with a push-pull output stage using grid biasing. One circuit uses solid-state rectifiers, while the other uses a tube rectifier.

The power transformer is the heart of the supply. It must be compatible with the AC power supplied (120VAC in the US), and provide the voltages and currents needed by the various sections of the amplifier. Referring to Figure 2.34, you can see that the primary of the power transformer connects to the AC power. A fuse is placed in series with one of the primary leads, and the power switch is in series with the other. The value of the fuse depends on the power used by the amplifier, but is usually 1-4A. Some amplifiers have one or more additional fuses in the secondary circuits to better protect the power transformer from component and other failures.

**Figure 2.34** Power Supply with Solid-State Rectifier

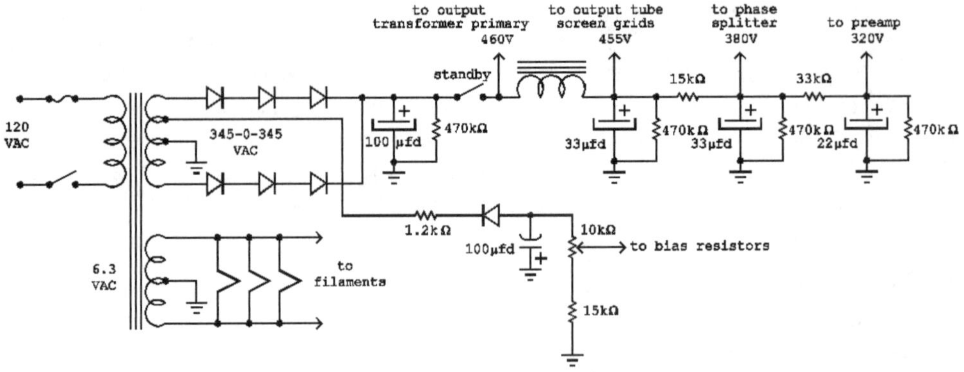


The power transformer in Figure 2.34 has two secondaries. One is a 6.3VAC center-tapped filament supply. It must be able to supply enough current for all of the tubes used in the amplifier, with a reasonable margin for safety. The center tap is connected to ground to ensure that the DC voltage at the filaments stays close to ground. This in turns avoids the potential for excessive filament-to-cathode voltages in the grounded-cathode stages, which can cause tube failure. However, if any of the cathodes are at an elevated DC potential (for example, in a cathode follower stage), an additional filament winding, biased to a higher DC potential, may be needed.

If the filament winding is not center-tapped, it can still be biased to ground by connecting resistors from each leg to ground. A value around 100Ω is often used.

The center-tapped high-voltage secondary feeds a full-wave rectifier with three diodes in series in each leg. The peak voltage at the output of the secondary can be quite high, and using several diodes in series reduces the voltage across each diode, improving reliability. The voltage drop across the diodes is insignificant when compared to the high power supply voltages generated. A *snubbing* capacitor can be connected in parallel with each diode to ensure that equal voltages appear across each diode and to reduce noise generated by the diodes.

The output of the rectifier is connected to the first filter capacitor and the standby switch, which serves several purposes:

— If a solid-state rectifier is employed, you can use the standby switch to disconnect the plate voltage until the filaments warm up and begin emitting electrons. This can prevent damage to the tubes, although this is not a problem in most amplifiers. If a tube rectifier is used, the high voltage is delayed until the rectifier tube's filament warms up, and there is no need for a standby switch for this purpose.

— You can turn off the plate voltage when guitars or effects are plugged in and out of the amplifier, eliminating buzzing and other noises.

— You can leave the amplifier permanently on in the standby mode, and can then switch it fully on immediately when desired. Operating the amplifier in this manner will often increase component life, as many failures occur when switching on. It does waste power, however.

The other pole of the standby switch is connected to the center tap of the output transformer and the choke, which in turn is connected to subsequent filter stages. The function of the filter stages is to smooth the rectifier output sufficiently for use in the various amplifier stages. To understand how this occurs refer to Figure 2.35.

**Figure 2.35** Filter Capacitor Charging and Discharging

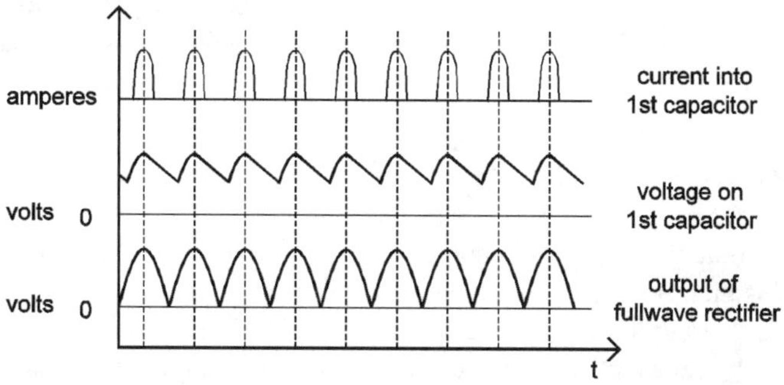


The bottom curve in Figure 2.35 shows the output of the full-wave rectifier. Each waveform peak charges the capacitor to the peak voltage $V_P$. However, as current is fed to the amplifier the voltage on the capacitor decreases until the next input peak occurs, at which time it increases again to $V_P$. This is illustrated in the second curve of Figure 2.35, where the voltage on the capacitor equals $V_P$ when the rectifier output reaches its peak, but then decreases linearly (assuming constant current being drawn from the supply) until the next peak occurs, at which time the voltage again increases to $V_P$. This is called a *sawtooth* waveform, and the amplitude of the AC component (the sawtooth) compared to the average DC voltage determines the amount of *ripple* on the DC voltage. Since larger value capacitors store more charge than smaller value capacitors, when sourcing the same current a larger capacitor will create less ripple than a smaller capacitor.

Since current passes through the diodes only when the voltage at the cathode is lower than the voltage at the anode, they will conduct only a fraction of the time, when the rectifier output is near its peak value and the capacitor has discharged sufficiently so that its voltage is lower than the rectifier output voltage. This creates spikes of current, as shown in the upper curve of Figure 2.35. These spikes can be quite high, and can cause hum and noise to be generated.

The first filter capacitor's value is chosen so that, with a given current being supplied to the output stage, the ripple is small enough to avoid introducing objectionable hum in the output. If the output stage is push-pull, 10-20% ripple is acceptable, since the output transformer cancels most of the ripple current. Single-ended output stages require less ripple. For low-power amplifiers, 10-20ufd is usually adequate, while for high-power amplifiers 47-100ufd is often used, since their output stages draw significantly more current. A higher-value capacitor results in a tighter, stiffer sound, while a supply with a lower-value capacitor sounds looser, causing a compression-like effect when playing loudly. This effect is particularly noticeable when playing lower notes. If the capacitor value is too high, large current spikes occur when the capacitor is charged, creating noise. Also, if you use a tube rectifier, a maximum value for the capacitor is specified to prevent excessive current in the tube.

Special capacitors are used in power supplies. They must withstand high voltages, and relatively high values are often required. To achieve this performance economically, *electrolytic* capacitors are usually specified. Electrolytic capacitors are polarized, that is, one terminal must be kept positive with respect to the other for proper operation. If an electrolytic capacitor is connected backwards, it can fail catastrophically, often by exploding. Electrolytic capacitors are marked, usually with a "-" on the terminal that is normally grounded, and designs that incorporate them are marked to indicate proper orientation in the circuit. You can see the markings in Figure 2.34.

If no current is drawn from the 100ufd capacitor, the voltage at the capacitor will equal the peak voltage output from the rectifier. If the transformer secondary is rated for $345V_{rms}$, the peak voltage is then about 485V. Under load, however, the voltage is somewhat less, in this case about 460V, due to resistance in the transformer secondary winding and magnetic losses in the transformer.

The voltage on the first capacitor is further filtered by the inductor and the next capacitor, which together form a second-order low-pass filter, providing a smooth DC voltage to the screen grids of the output tubes. The inductor allows DC to pass, but its impedance rises with frequency, so AC signals are blocked increasingly as their frequency rises. The capacitor shunts AC signals to ground, further reducing their levels. The predominant AC frequency is 120 Hz from the full-wave rectifier, so you should use a large value inductor to provide a high impedance at that frequency. If you use an 8 H inductor, its impedance at 120 Hz is 6k Ω, which, in conjunction with the 33 ufd capacitor, reduces the 120 Hz signal level by around 40 dB.

The inductor and the 33 ufd capacitor also form a *resonant circuit,* whose output rises at its resonant frequency before falling at higher frequencies. The resonant frequency is determined by the values of the inductor and capacitor, and should be well below any audio frequencies of interest to avoid instability. You can calculate the resonant frequency using the formula:

$$f = \frac{1}{2\pi\sqrt{LC}} \quad \textbf{Equation 2.7}$$

With L = 8 H and C = 33 ufd, the resonant frequency is 9.8 Hz. The amount of boost provided at the resonant frequency depends on the DC resistance in the circuit, primarily in the inductor. The large inductors used in power supplies usually have DC resistance of hundreds of ohms, which results in a relatively small boost. The DC resistance also causes a voltage drop across the inductor, so the voltage at the 33 ufd capacitor will be slightly lower than the voltage at the 100 ufd capacitor, about 455 V in this case.

Generally, you want to use the highest-value inductor possible, as this will provide the greatest 120 Hz attenuation and will also result in the lowest possible resonant frequency for the LC filter. A resistor can be used in place of the inductor, but the 120 Hz attenuation will be reduced, resulting in more hum in the output. However, in some designs you may want the screen grid voltage to be significantly lower than the plate voltage, in which case you can use a resistor (together with an inductor if desired) to lower the voltage.

Most of the current from the power supply flows to the output tubes. A typical 50W push-pull output stage will draw a quiescent current of around 70mA for the plates and another 10mA for the screen grids. Peak currents will be higher. The rest of the stages will use as little as 5mA of current in total. So, the inductor should be capable of handling at least 25mA of current.

Following the 33ufd capacitor we have two more RC filter stages. The first, consisting of a 15kΩ resistor and another 33ufd capacitor, supplies the phase splitter stage. If the combined quiescent current in the phase splitter, input and second amplifier stages is 5mA, 75V will drop across the 15kΩ resistor, causing the voltage at the second 33ufd capacitor to be about 380V. The last filter stage, consisting of a 33kΩ resistor and a 22ufd capacitor, feeds the input amplifier and the second amplifier stage. Since these two stages use about 1.8mA of current, the voltage drop across the 33kΩ resistor will be 60V, resulting in a voltage at the 22ufd capacitor of around 320V.

You can see from Figure 2.34 that the DC voltages feeding the stages are isolated or *decoupled* from each other, and that the DC voltages feeding the early stages, where signal levels are low, are filtered more than the DC voltages feeding later stages. This design helps to reduce noise in the circuit, and also prevents signals in one section of the amplifier from affecting signals in other sections, which can cause oscillation and distortion.

The 470kΩ resistors in parallel with each filter capacitor discharge the capacitors when the power is turned off. If no path is provided to *bleed* the voltage to ground, the capacitors can remain charged for days or weeks, which can be dangerous when working on the amplifier.

The final part of the power supply, consisting of a 1.2kΩ resistor, a diode, a 100ufd capacitor, and a 10kΩ potentiometer in series with a 15kΩ resistor produces the negative DC voltage required to bias the output stage. A lower-voltage tap is provided in the secondary of the power transformer, which is rectified by the diode and charges up the 100ufd capacitor. Note that the 100ufd capacitor has its positive terminal connected to ground. The resistors and potentiometer are chosen so that the voltage available at the wiper of the potentiometer is in a suitable range for the output tubes used. This varies from as little as -6VDC (for the 6BQ5, as we have already seen), to -70VDC or more for other output tubes. The 1.2kΩ resistor also protects the power transformer by limiting current if a component, for example the 100ufd capacitor, fails.

A similar circuit utilizing a tube rectifier is shown in Figure 2.36. Note the third secondary winding, which supplies 5VAC for the rectifier filament. Since the supply voltage is taken from the cathode, the filament is at a high DC voltage, and thus must be separate from the other filament supply, notwithstanding that it is a different voltage.

Tube rectifiers have a specified maximum value for the first capacitor. For the 5AR4/GZ34 shown in Figure 2.36, the first capacitor value should be no higher than 60ufd. Using a higher value capacitor results in excessive peak currents and premature tube failure.

Tube rectifiers also have internal DC resistance, which results in a lower output voltage than from a solid-state rectifier fed the same secondary voltage. The 5AR4/GZ34's internal resistance is 150-200Ω, so if the amplifier draws a total of 100mA of current, around 20V drops across the tube rectifier. This is the primary reason why tube rectified circuits sound different from solid-state rectified circuits. When playing loud, the circuit draws more current and the supply voltage *sags*, causing a kind of compression. Note that this effect occurs primarily in push-pull amplifiers, where the output stage current draw varies with signal level.

Tube rectifier supply sag can be simulated in power supplies with solid-state rectifiers by adding a resistor in series with the output of the rectifier. The value can be chosen by listening, but is often 100-200Ω, similar to the plate resistance of a rectifier tube.

The rest of the circuit is similar to that of Figure 2.34.

**Figure 2.36** Typical Power Supply with Tube Rectifier

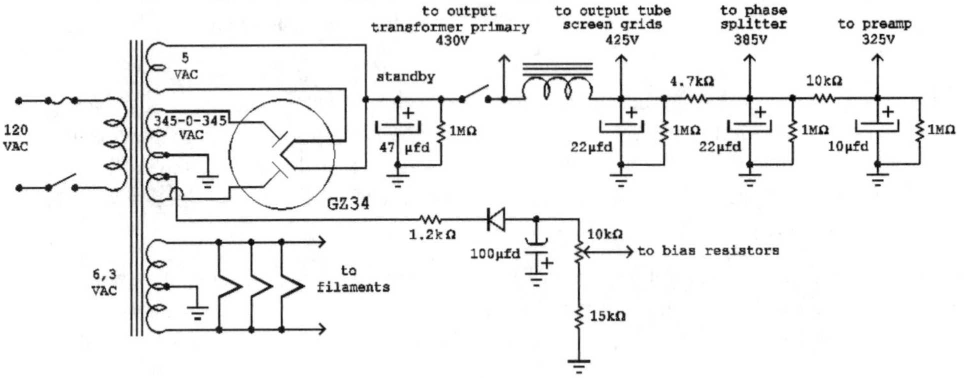

# Chapter 3
# Effects

Many guitar amplifiers include the ability to modify the signal beyond simply adjusting the tonal balance. The general term for this is *signal processing,* and a wide variety of signal processors are available in a variety of implementations. *Effects* are created using signal processors.

We will call signal processors incorporated in the amplifier *on-board* processors. We will call those implemented outside of the amplifier *external* processors.

External processors can be placed between the guitar and the amplifier, for example in a foot pedal, or an *effects loop* can be used to place the processor later in the signal path within the amplifier. Each of these approaches has advantages and disadvantages, and will be discussed later in this chapter. You can see block diagrams of the three approaches in Figure 3.1.

**Figure 3.1** Effects Implementations

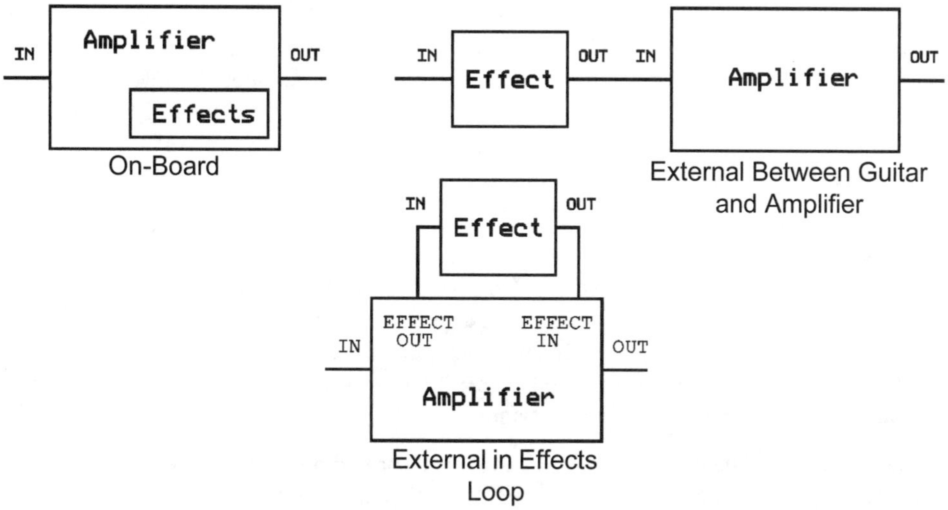


Some signal processors can be effectively implemented on-board in tube amplifiers, while others are best implemented externally due to their complexity. The most common on-board effects are reverberation, tremolo, and overdrive. This chapter discusses each of these in detail, followed by a section on effects loop implementation and use.

## Maintaining Signal Integrity

Before we begin exploring the various effects circuits, we need to understand how signal processing affects a signal apart from creating the desired effect. Any circuitry in the signal path affects the sound, including tubes, other components, and amplifier or signal processing stages. The effect of components will be discussed in Chapter 4.

More importantly, routing through a signal processor can change dynamics, noise, distortion, and level. As we discussed in Chapter 2, the input and output characteristics of each amplifier stage must be chosen to match the preceding and following stages. Level, gain and impedance must be carefully considered to ensure proper signal handling and overload characteristics. Any added signal processing can disturb these relationships and degrade the signal, even with the effect turned off.

The ways in which a signal processor can affect amplifier performance are:

— Input impedance – If the processor is external and located between the guitar and amplifier, its input impedance must be high enough to load the guitar output properly, but not so high as to cause excessive high-frequency roll-off and noise. If the processor is external and located in a properly designed effects loop, the effects loop driver should have low source impedance so that any external processor used will be properly driven. If on-board, the processor should be designed to properly load the driving stage. Effects loops and on-board processor design are discussed later in this chapter.

— Input signal handling – Most external processors have a buffer amplifier immediately after the input, in part to provide the proper input impedance, as noted above. When the processor is located between the guitar and the amplifier, this buffer must be able to handle input signal levels of at least 1-2V peak-to-peak with adequate headroom. Since most effects pedals operate from a 9VDC supply, the maximum peak-to-peak voltage everywhere in the device must be somewhat less than 9V, leaving little headroom in the pedal. If the device offers gain, as is often the case, this problem is exacerbated. In order to prevent clipping in the input amplifier, the signal is often attenuated at the input. External effects processors that operate in an effects loop are usually powered by 120VAC, and usc power supplies that can provide adequate headroom throughout the device.

— Noise – Effects processors can generate noise, especially pedals. This is due to the relatively low signal levels and the high-gain amplifier stages used in many circuits, including distortion pedals and compressors. Effects processors using time delay, including reverberation, chorus, flanging, and delay, can also be noisy, depending on how the delay is generated. Attenuating and then re-amplifying the input signal also generates noise. Again, outboard processors powered from 120VAC and intended for use in an effects loop can produce less noise if properly designed.

— Output level – The processor must be capable of providing the proper signal level to the following stage. Pedal processor output levels are again limited by the supply voltage, so if the pedal provides gain you can easily overload the output amplifier, causing distortion. However, since pedals normally feed the guitar input of the amplifier, output levels can be kept low to avoid this problem. The output level of an external processor placed in an effects loop can easily overload the effects input of the amplifier, depending on the design. However, most processors have an output level control that can be adjusted to provide the proper signal level.

— Output impedance – Some processors, particularly non-powered units such as volume pedals, have relatively high output impedance. Changing the control settings can change the output impedance. Most properly-designed powered pedals and processors used in effects loops have low output impedance, which eliminates this problem. If a processor with high output impedance is connected to a device with low input impedance, its output level, dynamic range, and frequency response can be affected. This can happen when pedals are connected in series.

In order to avoid some of the problems mentioned above, many effects processors have *hard bypass* capability, which means that the entire device can be bypassed when the effect is switched off. This is normally done using a bypass switch, so the input signal is disconnected from the effects circuit and routed directly to the output jack. Even in this case, however, the processor can affect the signal, due to the extra cable used, the switch, and the input and output connectors.

When you use external effects processors, you must be aware of all of these potential problems and carefully consider the types of effects, order of effects, gain settings, power supply, and the interconnection scheme used. In general, the simpler the path the less chance that signal integrity will be compromised.

Internal effects processors can be designed to properly interface with the rest of the circuit, avoiding many of the potential problems mentioned above. However, as you will see in the following sections, internal effects processors inevitably affect the rest of the amplifier.

## Distortion

Distortion is fundamental to many guitarists' tone palettes. However, achieving good-sounding distortion is not easy. You must first understand the various types of distortion and their characteristics. Further, deciding whether a particular type of distortion sounds good or bad is subjective, and part of the art of playing the electric guitar. Finally, once you know what kind of distortion you want, you must determine how to achieve it.

This section discusses distortion generated by different circuits. We will confine our discussion to harmonic distortion, excluding hum and noise, both of which are undesirable in most situations.

In most audio circuits, harmonic distortion is either *even-order* or *odd-order.* Remember from Chapter 1 that harmonic distortion components are integer multiples of the fundamental frequency. Even-order harmonics are even integer multiples (2, 4, 6, and so on), while odd-order harmonics are odd integer multiples (3, 5, 7, and so on). The amplitude of harmonic distortion components usually decreases as their integer number increases. The first few harmonics are generally greatest in amplitude and have the biggest effect on the sound.

The amplifier stage of Figure 2.5 operates along load line AB of Figure 2.6, which is reproduced below as Figure 3.2.

This amplifier produces distortion at all levels, with the amount of distortion increasing dramatically as signals approach the ends of the load line (points A and B).

**Figure 3.2** Typical 12AX7A amplifier stage operating characteristics

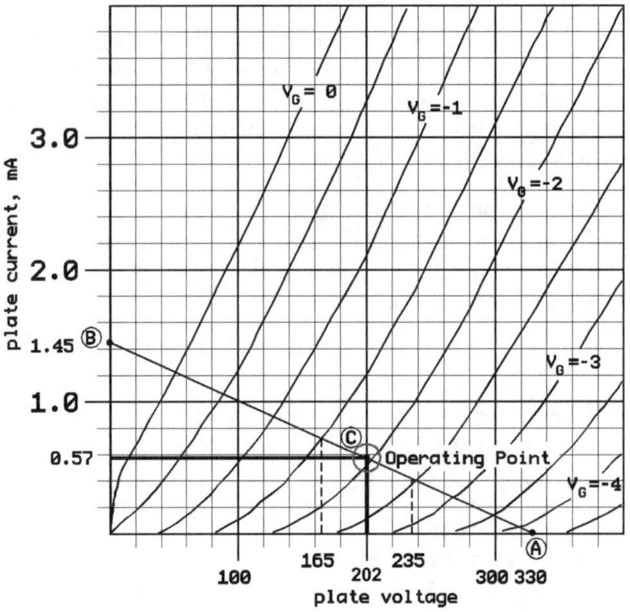


Distortion at low and medium signal levels is created because equal positive and negative input signals produce unequal plate voltages. To see why this occurs refer to Figure 3.2, and assume an input voltage of 3 V peak-to-peak. The DC voltage at the grid varies from -0.5 VDC to -3.5 VDC, since the quiescent bias operating point is -2 VDC. On the positive-going portion of the wave, the plate voltage varies from 202 VDC (the plate voltage at the quiescent operating point) to 88 VDC (the plate voltage when the grid is at -0.5 VDC), a difference of 114 V. On the negative-going portion of the wave, the plate voltage varies from 202 VDC to 298 VDC (the plate voltage when the grid is at -3.5 VDC), a difference of 96 V. So, the two halves of the output waveform are different, which by definition means it is distorted. This concept is illustrated in Figure 3.3.

**Figure 3.3** Input Waveform and Resulting Asymmetric Output Waveform

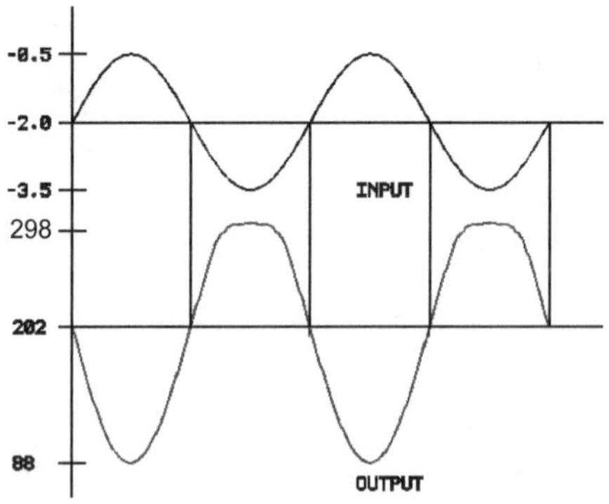


The harmonic distortion produced by a class A stage is primarily even-order. The second harmonic is one octave above the fundamental, and the fourth harmonic is two octaves above the fundamental. Thus, the most audible harmonics generated are closely related to the

fundamental. This means the distortion sounds musical, and you get relatively little dissonant distortion when two or more notes are played at the same time.

It is possible to calculate the amount of distortion (usually expressed as a percentage), but for our purposes it is sufficient to state that low-level distortion in typical amplifier stages is on the order of a few percent or less. Readers interested in calculating harmonic distortion (it can also be measured) are referred to the Touzelet article listed in the bibliography.

You can see by looking at Figure 3.2 that distortion is created because the characteristic curves get closer together as the grid voltage approaches cut-off and the plate voltage approaches its maximum. Therefore, stages with more negative quiescent bias voltages have higher distortion than those with more positive quiescent bias voltages, because the operating point is closer to the non-linear characteristic curves. However, stages with higher bias voltages have less input headroom. Also, you can see that close to the operating point, at low signal levels, the distortion is lowest because the characteristic curves are most evenly spaced around the operating point.

At high input signal levels distortion is created differently. Again referring to Figure 3.2, you can see that the tube cuts off if the grid voltage is lower than around -4.0V. This means that for any input voltage lower than -2.0V (remember, the grid is biased at -2.0V) the plate voltage remains at 320V. Likewise, when the input voltage exceeds +2.0V the plate current is at its maximum, the plate voltage is at its minimum (around 50V), and any further rise in input voltage has little effect on the plate voltage, resulting in a similar "squaring off" of the waveform. This effect can be seen in Figure 3.4.

**Figure 3.4** Output Waveform for High Level Input Signal

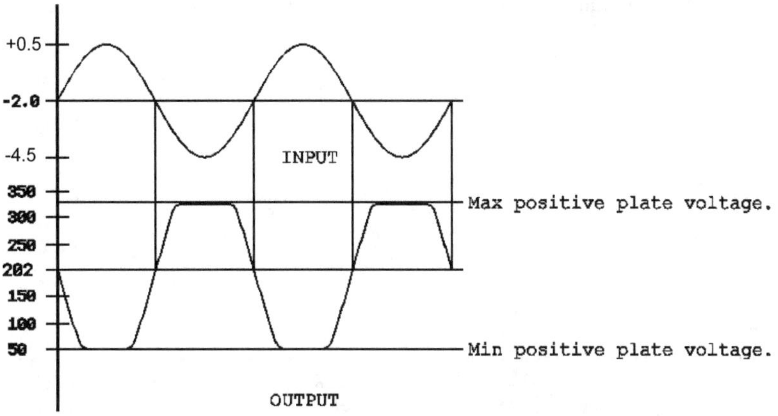


If the grid voltage becomes positive with respect to the cathode voltage, current can flow in the grid. This causes a change in the grid bias voltage, which in turn prevents the stage from passing signals until proper biasing has been restored. The time required to restore normal operation depends on the values of the grid circuit resistors and the coupling capacitor connected to the stage. This distortion mechanism only occurs on negative output voltage peaks in the presence of high input signal levels.

The distortion shown in Figure 3.4, sometimes referred to as *clipping,* has higher levels of odd-order harmonics. The third harmonic is an octave and a fifth above the fundamental, and the fifth harmonic is two octaves and a slightly-out-of-tune major third above the fundamental.

You can see that these relationships are more complex than those associated with even-order harmonic distortion, and they cause more dissonant distortion when multiple notes are played.

As discussed in Chapter 2, you should design each amplifier stage based on the desired gain, input and output, and distortion characteristics. However, since you usually want some distortion, even for "clean" amplifier settings, lower bias operating points are often preferable, including for the input stage, where substantial input headroom is required. Lower bias operating points also help avoid grid currents and the resulting harsh distortion generated in later stages when they are driven hard. We will discuss this concept further in the overdrive section of this chapter.

So far, our discussion has focused on single-ended, class A preamplifier stages. Output stages can also be driven to distortion, and the resulting tone can be very musical. Output stage distortion is different from preamplifier distortion in several important ways.

First, the output stage draws most of the current from the power supply. When the output stage is driven to distortion, supply current is at its maximum, and this can cause the supply voltage to *sag* (decrease when supply current is high) due to resistance in the secondary winding of the power transformer or the rectifier. This effect is particularly evident when tube rectifiers, which have an internal resistance of up to several hundred ohms, are used in the design. This signal-dependant supply variation results in a kind of compression or limiting of the signal, where gain is reduced for high-level signals due to the lower supply voltage.

Second, the impedance of the speaker loading the output transformer varies with frequency. Figure 3.5 shows the impedance of a typical 8Ω speaker in an open-back enclosure with respect to frequency.

**Figure 3.5** Impedance vs. Frequency for a Typical Guitar Amplifier Speaker

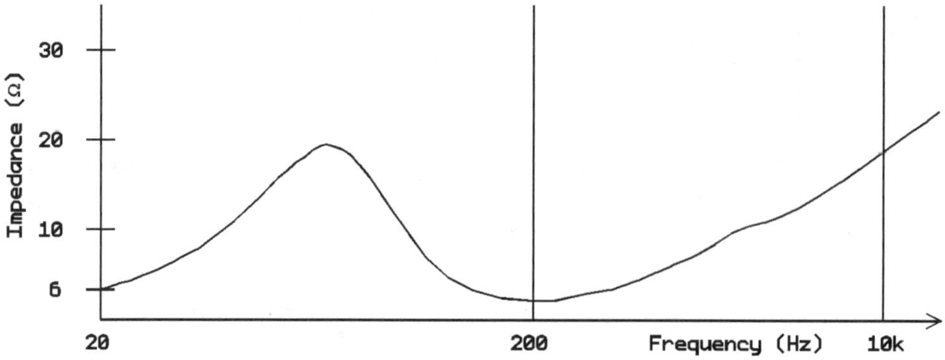


The low-frequency peak in Figure 3.5 is due to the mechanical resonance of the speaker, and is usually below the lowest note on the guitar. The rising impedance at higher frequencies is due to the inductance of the voice coil. As explained in Chapter 1, the primary impedance of the output transformer is the impedance connected to the secondary winding times the square of the turns ratio. So, the primary impedance of an output transformer connected to a typical speaker, and thus the output power and distortion characteristics, vary depending on the signal frequencies being amplified.

When driven hard, the speaker itself distorts, modifying the output signal of the amplifier, and also creates signals itself (due to the movement of the voice coil in the magnetic field) which are fed back to the amplifier. Further, at high sound levels the amplifier interacts acoustically with the guitar, creating a feedback loop that can be used expressively by a skilled guitarist.

Third, the output transformer affects the sound in several ways. As will be explained in Chapter 4, the response of the transformer at low and high frequencies varies with the power being delivered to the speaker. At high power levels, both low- and high-frequency response is reduced. The amount of reduction depends on the transformer used, but in many guitar amplifiers the reduction, especially in low frequency response, is audible. The transformer's magnetic core can saturate at high currents, affecting the sound in a manner similar to the power supply sag discussed earlier. Resistive and capacitive losses in the transformer can also affect its frequency response and power handling, but these effects are normally minor in a high-quality transformer.

Finally, as explained in Chapter 2, the feedback applied from the secondary of the output transformer to the phase splitter determines the gain of and reduces distortion in the output stage. More signal fed back reduces gain and distortion, and less feedback increases gain and distortion. The feedback can also be made frequency-dependant, as with the presence control of Figure 2.22.

If you use a push-pull output stage, any signal that is common to both phases is cancelled, as explained in Chapter 2. In a perfectly balanced PP output stage, even-order harmonic distortion generated in the output stage is cancelled, so odd-order harmonic distortion predominates. In actual amplifiers, balance is not perfect in the phase splitter, the two power tubes, or the output transformer, so even-order harmonic distortion components are not completely cancelled.

Another type of harmonic distortion, called *crossover distortion,* is also generated in PP output stages operating in class AB. Crossover distortion occurs when the signal waveform changes from negative to positive or vice versa, causing a switch in the output tube supplying current to the output transformer primary. Crossover distortion is generally not significant in guitar amplifiers. It can be minimized by careful component matching and choice of bias operating point.

In addition, distortion from earlier stages passes through the output stage unaltered.

This complex interaction of the guitar, power supply, speaker, and output stage has a big effect on the overall sound, and is the main reason why output stage distortion sounds so good. Skilled guitarists can control the distortion using the guitar's volume control, providing clean and overdriven tones.

The problem with output stage distortion is that the amplifier must be operated close to its maximum output level, which often is too loud for a given situation. One strategy to avoid excessive volume is to use an amplifier whose output power has been chosen so that, when it is operating at full power, its volume will be appropriate. For example, you might choose a 20W output stage like a Fender Deluxe when jamming in the garage, and use a 50W output stage like a Marshall in a club. In larger venues amplifiers are normally routed through the PA system, so any size can be used.

You can also use a *power soak* (or *attenuator*), which is a load connected to the speaker output with a variable output, which is connected to the speaker. The amplifier is turned up to generate output stage distortion, and then the power soak output level is adjusted for the desired volume. Unfortunately, power soaks do not load the amplifier output stage in the same way speakers do (although some are better than others), the acoustic interaction between the guitar and amplifier is reduced, and our hearing system responds differently at different levels, so the sound is different.

Another approach, discussed in the next section, provides more control over amplifier volume while still allowing distortion to be generated.

## Overdrive

Preamplifier stages can be overdriven to create distortion, as previously discussed in this chapter. The type of distortion generated depends on the input signal level and the design of the stage being overdriven. The primary advantage of generating distortion in the preamplifier is that the loudness of the amplifier can be controlled independently of the amount of distortion generated. Although the rich complexity and expressivity provided by an overdriven output stage is impossible to achieve, a properly designed overdrive circuit can be quite musical.

The simplest way to provide overdrive is to add a master volume control after the second preamplifier stage, as shown in Figure 2.17. You turn up the first volume control until the second preamplifier stage distorts as desired, and then adjust the master volume control for the desired loudness.

There are two major disadvantages to this approach. First, you usually have to drive the second stage into clipping to get enough distortion, in which case the distorted signal can sound harsh and unmusical. The tone controls can be adjusted but, since they are ahead of the overdriven stage in the circuit, they will be less effective.

Second, if you want to switch between clean and distorted tones, you must readjust both volume controls and possibly the tone controls every time you switch. This is impractical in a performance situation.

Finally, many guitarists prefer amplifiers with more gain than can be provided by two preamplifier stages.

An optimal overdrive circuit has the following characteristics:

— Rich, musical tone.

— The ability to adjust the tone of the overdrive channel without affecting the normal channel.

— Ample gain under all normal operating conditions.

— Independent volume controls for the normal and overdrive modes.

— The amplifier can be easily switched between normal and overdrive operation, and, when in the normal mode, the signal does not pass through the overdrive section.

The circuit of Figure 3.6 fulfills all of the requirements listed above.

We add two preamplifier stages, $V_{2A}$ and $V_{2B}$, providing a total of up to three stages that you can overdrive. Each stage is preceded by a level control. The goal is to drive each stage to close to its clipping point, generating predominantly second harmonic distortion. After passing through three such stages, the signal is sufficiently distorted, and has the desired richness and musicality.

The bias operating point for each stage is different, so the distortion generated by each stage will also be different, further enhancing the sound quality. The bias operating points and load lines for the four stages of the preamplifier of Figure 3.6 are shown in Figure 3.7.

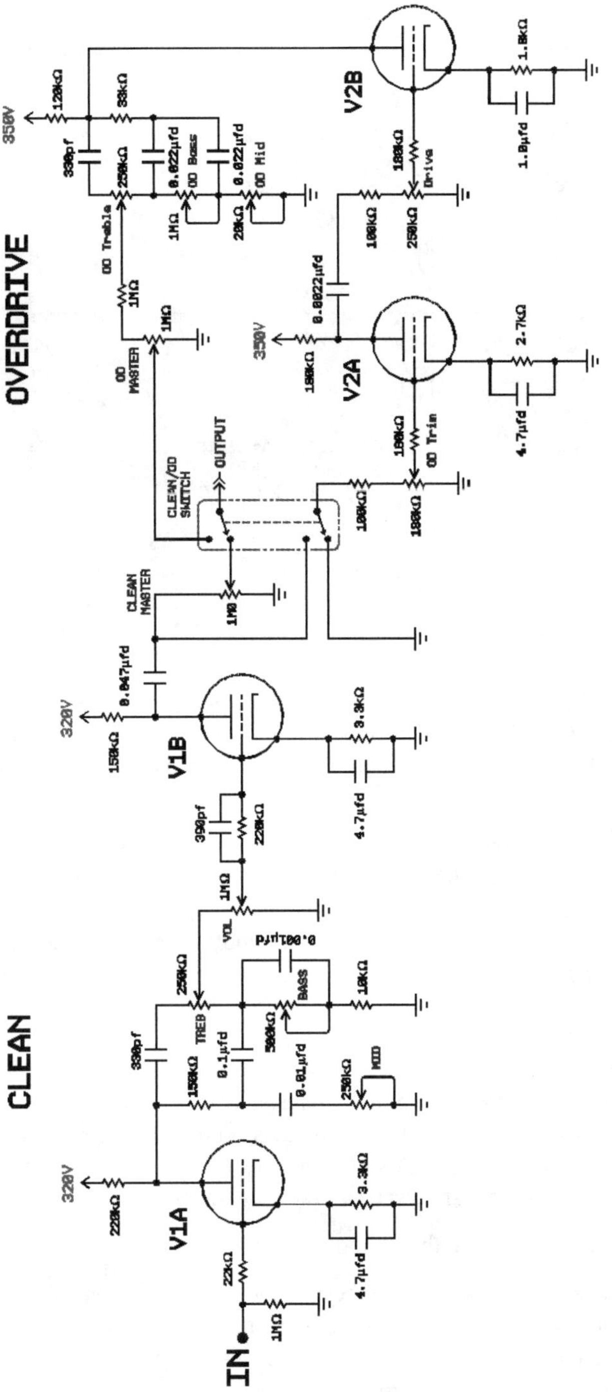


**Figure 3.6** Preamplifier with Overdrive

**Figure 3.7** Bias Operating Points and Load Lines for Overdrive Preamplifier

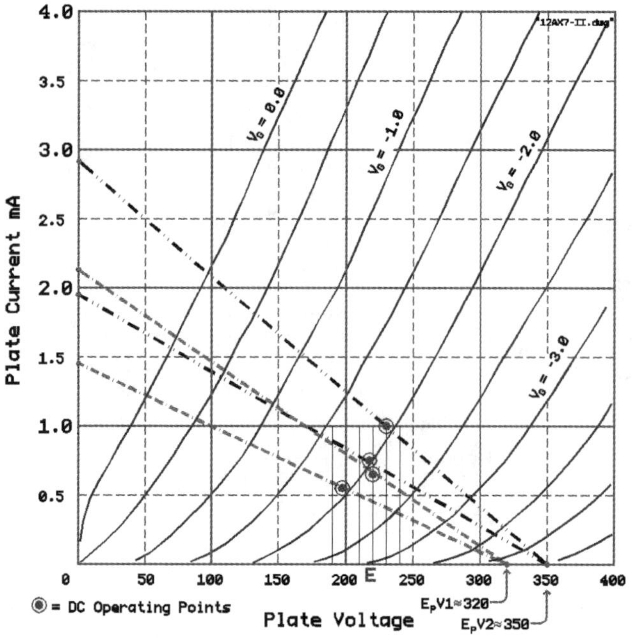


You can see that all of the operating points are clustered around a quiescent grid bias voltage of -2.0V. However, each load line has a different slope, and each bias operating point corresponds to a different quiescent plate current, so the distortion generated by each stage will be slightly different.

The output of $V_{2B}$ drives a second set of tone controls, so the overdrive tone can be adjusted independently of the clean channel tone. Note, however, that the clean channel tone controls and the volume control are all active when you engage the overdrive circuit. The tone controls are similar to the circuit of Figure 2.12, except that a middle control has been added. In the clean channel, a 250kΩ potentiometer has been added in series with the capacitor that normally bypasses the bass control, allowing limited adjustment of frequencies around 700Hz. A .001ufd capacitor has been added in parallel with the bass control to replace the bypass capacitor and ensure that the bass control does not affect high frequencies. The overdrive channel also includes a middle control. In this channel the resistor from the bottom of the bass control to ground is variable, providing limited boost and cut around 300Hz, depending on the setting of the bass control. Also, you can see that, unlike the clean channel, the overdrive channel has no output if the three tone controls are turned all the way down.

The simplest procedure for adjusting the various controls is as follows:

1. Adjust the clean channel controls for the desired clean sound. If some distortion is desired for the clean sound, you should set the Volume control fairly high. You adjust the overall volume with the Clean Master control. If you want less distortion, lower the Volume control and turn up the Clean Master control. The setting of the Volume control will affect the signal level at the grid of $V_{2A}$.

2. The OD Trim adjusts the signal level at the input of $V_{2A}$. Its setting depends on the setting of the Volume control, the output level of the guitar being amplified, and the amount and type of distortion desired. A good starting point is to adjust the OD Trim so that the level at the grid of $V_{2A}$ is about 15dB lower than the level at the plate of $V_{1B}$.
3. You then adjust the Drive control for the desired overall level of distortion, and the OD tone controls for the desired timbre.
4. Finally, adjust the OD Master control for the desired output level.

When the various level and tone controls are properly adjusted, this circuit will produce smooth, musical distortion with lots of sustain. If you want a more aggressive, clipped sound, you can turn up the level at one or more of the stages to produce clipping.

The Clean/OD Switch, which is normally implemented using a relay, completely removes the overdrive stages from the signal path when you switch to the clean mode. Note that the grid of $V_{2A}$ is grounded in the clean mode. This prevents the stage from oscillating and affecting the clean sound.

## Reverberation

The term *reverberation* refers to the natural phenomenon of sound waves reflecting off of walls, floors, ceilings, and other objects to create a *sound field.* The characteristics of the sound field depend on the environment, but in general sounds are followed by a number of closely-spaced echoes, which eventually decay to silence.

Signal processors create reverberation in a number of ways. The best units use digital signal processing, and are implemented as external processors as described at the beginning of this chapter.

On-board reverberation signal processors generally use a *spring reverb tank.* A spring reverb tank consists of an electrical-to-mechanical transducer connected to one or more springs. An electrical-to-mechanical transducer converts electrical power, such as the output of an amplifier, to mechanical motion, in this case back-and-forth motion of a piston. The springs are connected to the piston. The input impedance of the electrical-to-mechanical transducer varies from 8Ω to as much as 2.6kΩ, depending on the tank model chosen. As you will see, this is important when you design the drive amplifier.

The other ends of the springs are connected to a mechanical-to-electrical transducer. A mechanical-to-electrical transducer converts mechanical motion, in this case the back-and-forth motion of the springs, to electrical power. It is similar in construction to the electrical-to-mechanical transducer. The mechanical-to-electrical transducer normally has an output impedance of around 2kΩ. You can find a picture of typical spring reverb tanks in Chapter 4.

The reverberation processor is implemented as shown in Figure 3.8. The signal from the preamplifier is routed to a separate amplifier stage that drives the spring reverb tank's input. The tank's output is fed to another amplifier stage, and the output of that amplifier is mixed with the unprocessed (or *dry*) signal. As we will see later in this section, the characteristics of these amplifiers depend on a number of factors.

**Figure 3.8** Reverberation Processor Block Diagram

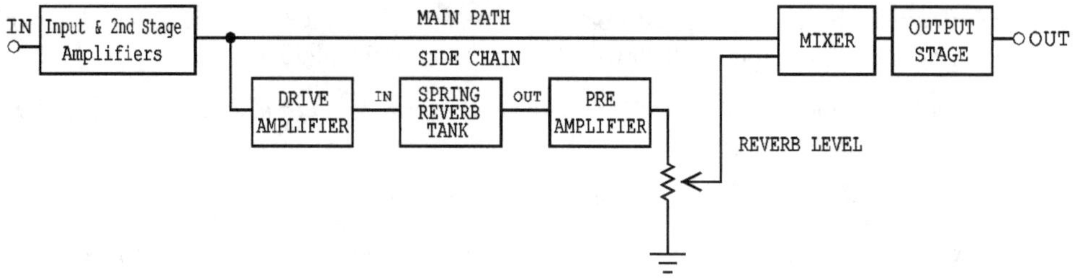


As you can see in Figure 3.8, the dry signal is routed directly to the mixer via the *main path.* The mixer simply adds the two signals together. The reverberation processor is placed in a *side chain,* which is in parallel with the main path. This helps maintain the integrity of the signal, especially since the dry signal constitutes most of the output of the mixer stage. The output of the side chain is fed to a level control and then mixed with the main path signal to create the *wet* signal, which is in turn fed to the output stage. Some reverberation processors also include a level control at the input to the drive amplifier, often referred to as the *dwell* control, and a tone control in the preamplifier stage. This is more common in external processors, where input signal conditions can vary.

You can design on-board reverberation processors using solid-state components with good results. Separate, lower-voltage power supplies are required. We will restrict our discussion to tube designs.

The first step in designing the drive amplifier is to choose a reverb tank. For our first design example, let's use the Accutronics Type 4 Model 4AB3C1B tank, which is used in many Fender amplifiers. Its input impedance is specified as 8Ω, and its output impedance is specified as 2.25kΩ. To drive the 8Ω input impedance, we use a low-power, SE, transformer-coupled power amplifier. The basic circuit is shown in Figure 3.9.

The output transformer has specified primary impedance of 22.8kΩ, and specified secondary impedance, as required by the reverb tank, of 8Ω. Its specified power handling capability is 3.5W.

The drive amplifier uses two 12AT7 tube sections in parallel. As we learned in Chapter 2, this doubles the current and power output capability of the stage compared to a stage utilizing a single 12AT7 section. The stage is cathode biased, and the cathode resistor is bypassed, as also discussed in Chapter 2. The characteristic curves, load line, and operating point for the stage are shown in Figure 3.10. The characteristic curves for two tubes operating in parallel are identical to those for a single tube, with the exception that the current figures on the y-axis are doubled.

**Figure 3.9** Typical Fender Reverb Drive Amplifier Design

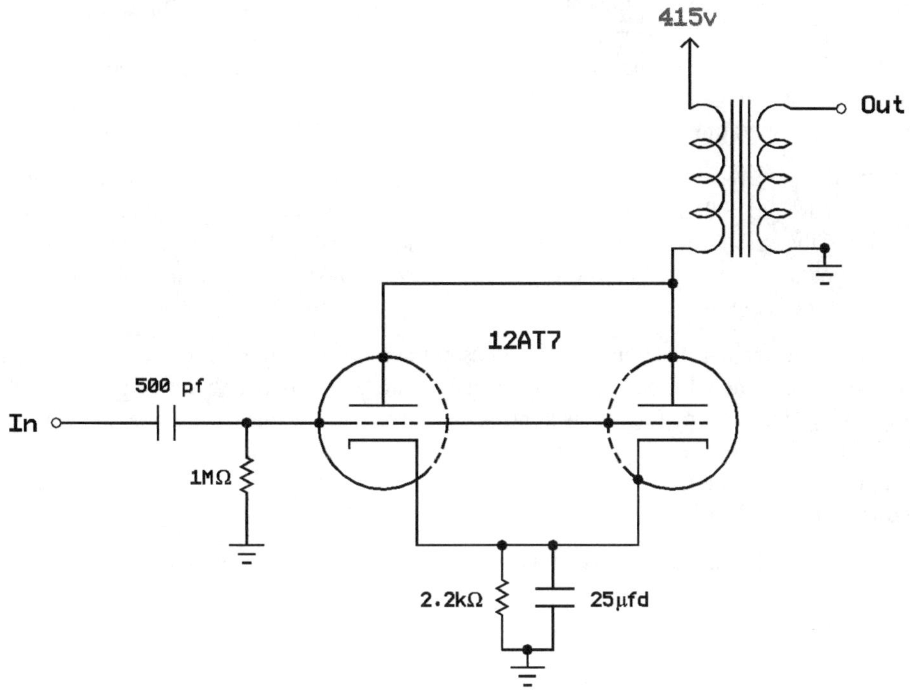


**Figure 3.10** Load Line and Operating Point for Drive Amplifier of Figure 3.9

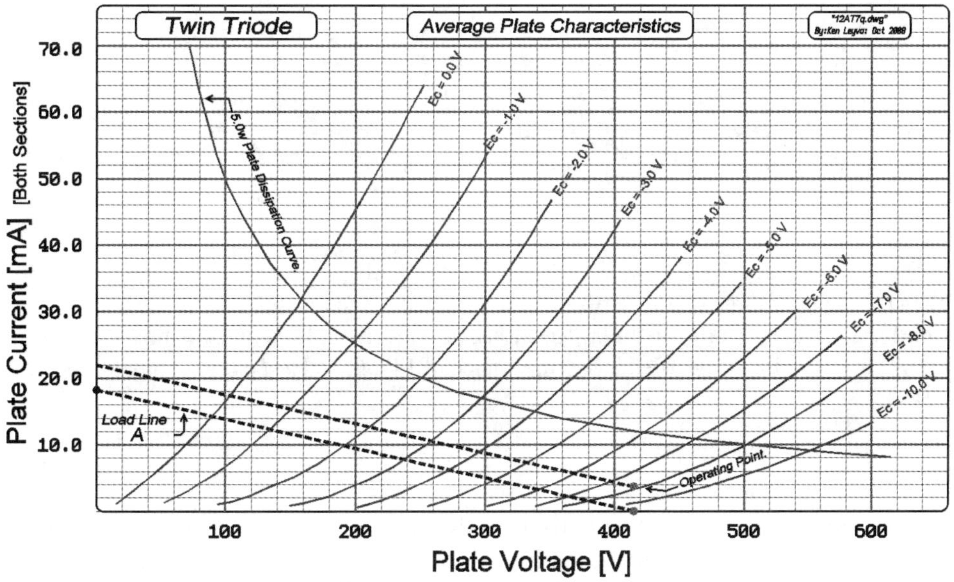


Load line A is defined by its two endpoints. One is the supply voltage (415V) at zero plate current, and the other is the supply voltage divided by the output transformer primary impedance (22.8kΩ), or 18.2mA, at zero plate voltage.

The stage as designed is not operated at maximum plate dissipation, so we must find the actual location of the load line using the cathode resistor value and the plate current to determine the quiescent grid voltage. The operating point is located where the plate current at 415V times the cathode resistor (2.2kΩ) equals the grid voltage. In this case, when the plate current is about 3.7mA, the grid voltage is about -8V, which fits the characteristic curves. You can see that the stage is always operating at well below its rated maximum plate dissipation.

The 500pfd input capacitor forms a HPF with the 1MΩ grid bias resistor. The filter has a cutoff point around 300Hz. This improves the sound of the reverberation, and helps to prevent overloading the spring reverb tank with low frequency signals. The cutoff frequency of the cathode bypass circuit is well below any frequency of interest, so it does not affect the response of the stage.

You can also design a drive amplifier that does not use a transformer. In this case, you need to use a reverb tank with a higher input impedance, to more closely match the output impedance of the driving stage. Ampeg uses this approach in many of their classic designs, including the GU-12. The GU-12 is a remarkable design because it uses a total of only five tubes (two in the PP output stage), yet includes reverb and tremolo. The reverb drive amplifier from the GU-12 is shown in Figure 3.11.

**Figure 3.11** Reverb Drive Amplifier from Ampeg GU-12

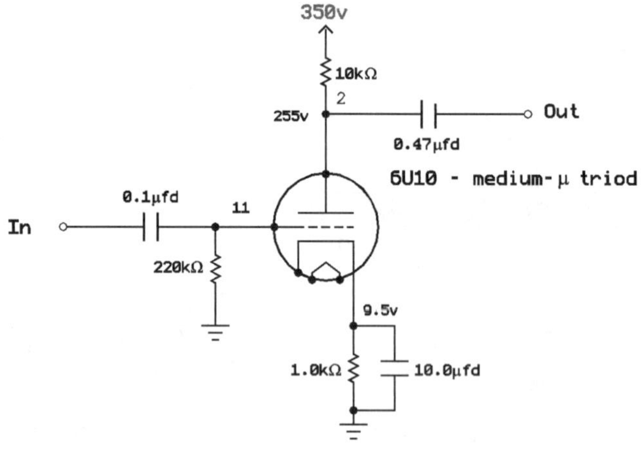


The 6U10 includes three sections, two medium-µ triodes and one high-µ triode. The drive amplifier utilizes one of the medium-µ sections. The reverb tank specified is the Accutronics 4FB3A1B, which has a specified input impedance of 1475Ω and a specified output impedance of 2250Ω.

The characteristics curves, load line, and operating point for this stage are shown in Figure 3.12.

The plate resistance for this section of the 6U10 is specified as 7700Ω, so the output impedance of the stage is 7700Ω in parallel with the plate resistor (10kΩ), or 4.3kΩ. This is not a perfect match to the input impedance of the reverb tank (1475Ω), which results in less-than-perfect coupling of the drive amplifier to the reverb tank. However, you can see from Figure 3.12 that the plate dissipation of the stage exceeds the maximum plate dissipation specification over part of the load line, so the plate resistor (and thus the output impedance) can not be lowered further. This cost-performance compromise results in less drive to the reverb tank, and therefore less "depth" to the reverb sound when compared to the previous example.

**Figure 3.12** Load Line and Operating Point for Drive Amplifier of Figure 3.11

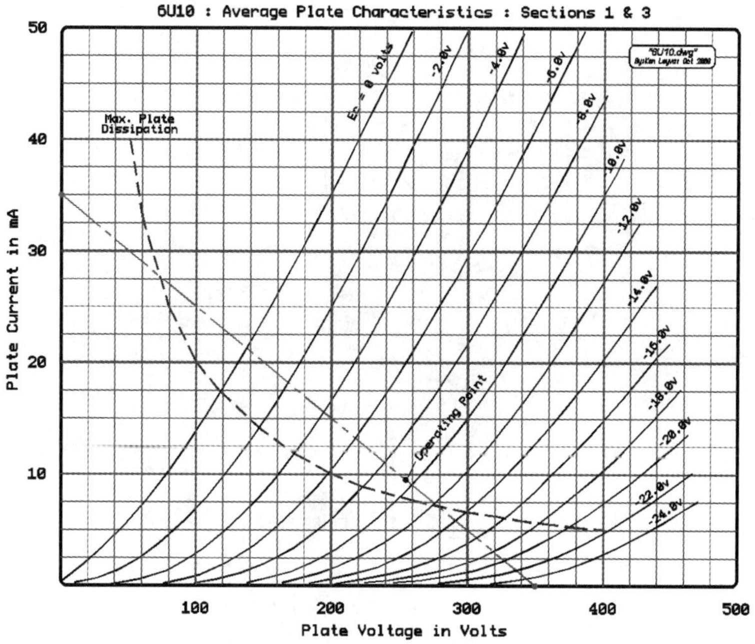


The input signal to the drive amplifier is taken from the output of the second stage amplifier, that is, the stage that follows the tone and volume controls, or a similar point in the preamplifier circuit. Because the input impedance of the drive amplifier is high (1MΩ for the Fender circuit and 220kΩ for the Ampeg circuit) it will have little effect on the output level of the second stage amplifier.

The output of the reverb tank is fed to a conventional gain stage, and then to a potentiometer to control the reverb level. The Fender and Ampeg stages are shown in Figure 3.13.

In the Fender circuit, the grid is biased to ground by the mechanical-to-electrical transducer in the reverb tank, and no grid stop resistor is provided. One cathode circuit is used for two stages, so the value of the cathode resistor is one-half the normal value, or 820Ω.

The Ampeg circuit does provide both grid biasing and grid stop resistors. This is a wise precaution, because the reverb tank is usually located some distance from the amplifier stage, and is connected to the stage with long shielded wires, increasing the chance of instability. Further, if the reverb tank is disconnected, the plate current could rise to catastrophic levels if the grid is not biased to ground. Both of these potential problems are addressed by the input resistors. The .005ufd capacitor connected from the grid to the cathode circuit further enhances stability by shunting high frequencies to ground through the 6.4ufd cathode bypass capacitor.

**Figure 3.13** Fender and Ampeg Reverb Output Preamplifiers

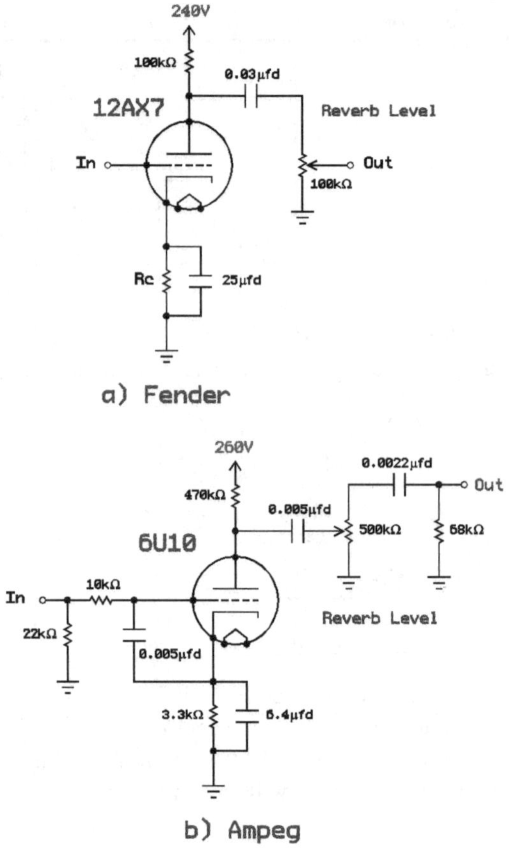


The output of the stage is connected to the wiper of the reverb level control, which forms a frequency-dependant voltage divider with the .002ufd capacitor and the 68kΩ resistor. These two components form a HPF with a cut-off frequency of about 1.2kHz, so low frequency signals from the reverb tank are attenuated.

The output of the reverberation processor is combined with the main path signal in the mixer. You can mix the two signals in any proportion desired, and you can choose the overall gain of the stage as needed. A typical mixer stage, used in Fender amplifiers, is shown in Figure 3.14.

Since no current flows into the grid, you can think of the input circuit as two voltage dividers. The second stage amplifier output goes through a voltage divider whose series element is 3.3MΩ and whose shunt element is 220kΩ in parallel with 470kΩ, or 150kΩ. Note that this is only true when the reverb level control is all the way down, but the difference will be minor in other settings, as the reverb level control is small with respect to the 470kΩ resistor. So, the second stage amplifier output is attenuated by $\frac{150}{3300+150}$, or 27dB.

**Figure 3.14** Fender Mixer Stage Circuit Diagram

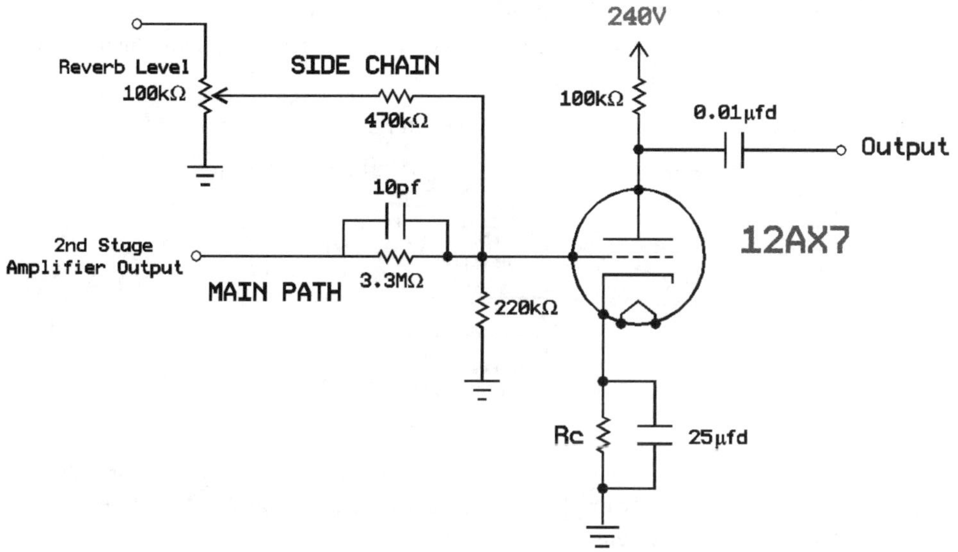


The reverb preamp output goes through a voltage divider whose series element is 470kΩ (again, varying slightly depending on the setting of the reverb level control) and whose shunt element is 220kΩ in parallel with 3.3MΩ, or 206kΩ. So the reverb preamplifier output is attenuated by 10dB.

Both signals are then amplified by the amplifier stage, which has a gain of about 36dB, so at the output of the mixer the second stage amplifier signal has been increased by about 9dB and the reverb preamplifier signal has been increased by about 26dB. Both of these overall gains can be adjusted as desired by changing the values of the various resistors in the input circuit. If you raise the value of the 3.3MΩ resistor, the dry signal gain will be lowered, and if you lower it the gain will be raised. Likewise, if you raise the value of the 470kΩ resistor the reverb signal gain will be lowered, and if you lower it the gain will be raised. If you raise the value of the 220kΩ resistor the gain of both signals it be raised, and if you lower it the gain will be lowered.

The 10pfd capacitor across the 3.3MΩ resistor will increase the gain of the dry signal at higher frequencies, starting around 4.8kHz. If you raise the value of the capacitor the high frequencies will be boosted starting at a lower frequency, and if you lower the value the boost will start at a higher frequency.

The mixer circuit used in the Ampeg GU-12 is similar to the one in Figure 3.14, although the component values and circuit topology are slightly different.

You can switch the reverberation processor on and off by shorting either the input to the reverb preamplifier or the output of the reverb driver to ground using a footswitch.

## Tremolo

Tremolo is a periodic variation in volume, not to be confused with *vibrato,* which is a periodic variation in frequency. Unfortunately, Fender and other manufacturers refer to their tremolo effect as vibrato, lending to the confusion.

The block diagram of a tremolo processor is shown in Figure 3.15.

**Figure 3.15** Tremolo Processor Block Diagram

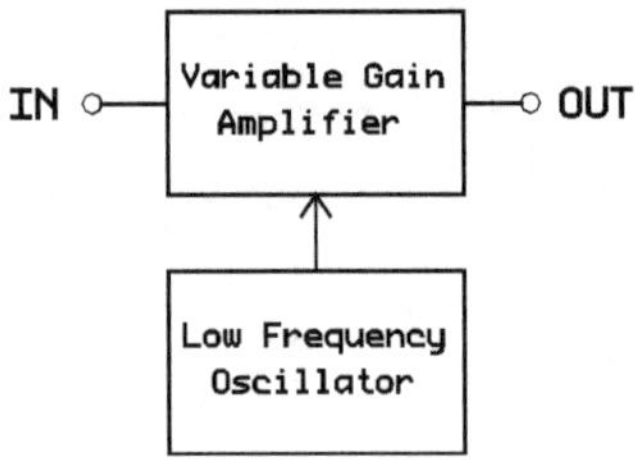


You can implement each block in a number of ways. As with the reverb processor, solid-state solutions are possible, especially for the *low-frequency oscillator (LFO*). As before, we will limit our discussion to tube designs.

The LFO is usually implemented using a *phase-shift oscillator* circuit. In a phase-shift oscillator, the output is fed back to the input after being shifted in phase by 360 degrees. The amplifier stage itself shifts the phase by 180 degrees, because the signal at the plate is out-of-phase with the signal at the grid. A phase-shifting network is connected to the output to provide an additional 180 degrees of phase shift. The frequency of oscillation is the frequency at which the signal is shifted exactly 360 degrees, and is determined by the component values in the phase-shifting network. As long as the overall gain of the circuit is greater than one, it will oscillate. The general circuit is shown in Figure 3.16.

As explained in Chapter 1, a simple RC network shifts the phase of the output signal by up to 90 degrees. Since the filter never quite reaches 90 degrees of phase shift, three RC networks in series are necessary to provide 180 degrees of total phase shift. Normally, the three sections are identical, with each chosen to provide 60 degrees of phase shift at the desired oscillation frequency. In addition to shifting the phase, the network also attenuates the signal substantially (usually around 30dB), so the tube must have sufficient gain to provide an overall gain greater than one. If the overall gain is less than one, the circuit will not sustain oscillation.

In a tremolo circuit, the LFO must be variable, that is, the frequency of oscillation must be adjustable over a range of around 3Hz-10Hz. The best way to provide this capability is to change all three sections of the network together, using a three-section potentiometer, as shown with the dotted lines in Figure 3.16. However, designers often use a single potentiometer, resulting in substantial cost savings.

The variable oscillator design used in many Fender amplifiers is shown in Figure 3.17.

The first half of the circuit in Figure 3.17 is the LFO. Positive feedback is applied to the grid via the network discussed above. The first RC circuit is the .02ufd plate coupling capacitor and the 3MΩ speed control in series with the 100kΩ resistor. The second and third RC circuits consist of a .01ufd capacitor and a 1MΩ resistor. The stage is cathode biased, as usual. The cathode bypass capacitor must be large to prevent low-frequency roll-off in the oscillation frequency range.

**Figure 3.16** Phase-Shift Oscillator

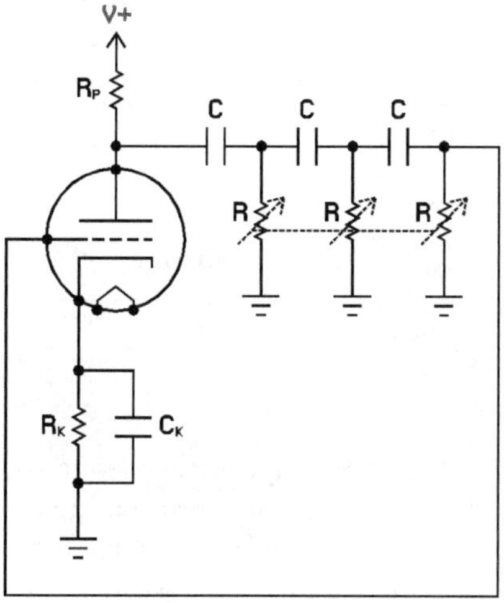


**Figure 3.17** Fender Tremolo Circuit

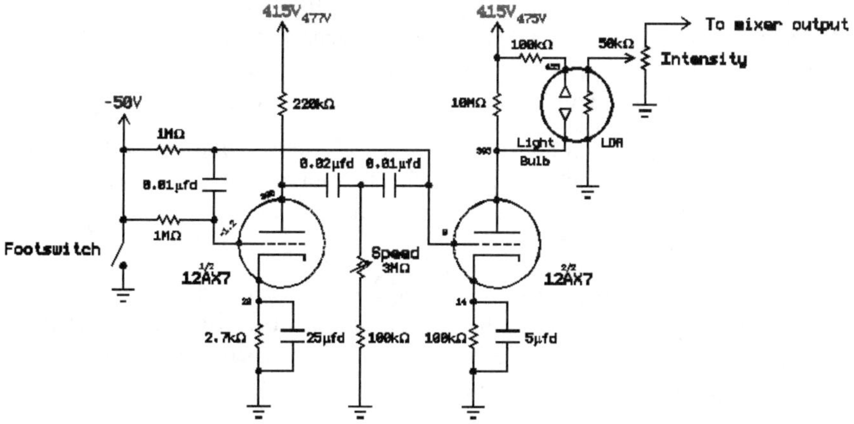


The overall gain of the circuit must be greater than one to support oscillation, so we use a 12AX7A section, which has a gain of up to 100. Assuming sufficient overall gain, oscillation will occur at the frequency at which the three RC sections provide 180 degrees of phase shift. Using equation 1.16, we can see that the second and third sections of the network will shift the phase 60 degrees at about 10 Hz, so this circuit will operate in our frequency range of interest. Changing the resistance of the speed control varies the phase shift of the first RC section, which in turn changes the oscillation frequency.

When the footswitch is open, the grid of the tube is biased to a negative voltage (through a large value resistor), cutting it off and turning off the LFO. Grounding the grid biasing resistor puts the section in its normal operating mode.

You can also design the variable gain amplifier in a number of ways. One approach commonly used in older and low-cost guitar amplifiers uses the LFO output to vary the bias on the grids of the output tubes. Changing the bias voltage causes the output level to vary, creating the tremolo effect. The tremolo circuit used in the Ampeg J-12 is shown in Figure 3.18.

**Figure 3.18** Bias Modulation Tremolo Circuit

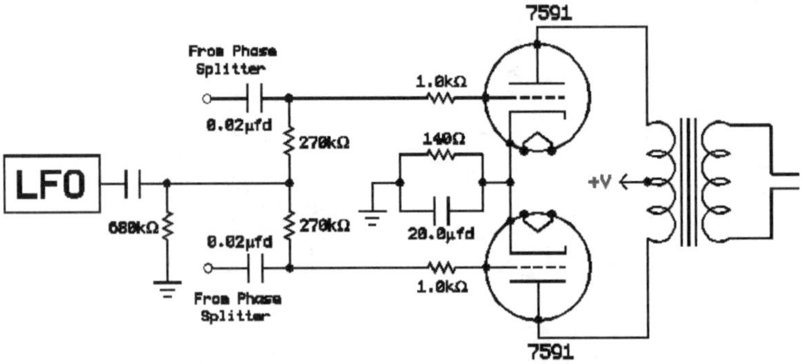


You can see in Figure 3.18 that the output stage is cathode-biased, so the grids of the output tubes are referenced to ground. The 1kΩ grid stop resistors are connected to 270kΩ biasing resistors, the other ends of which are connected together and then to ground via a 680kΩ resistor. If the LFO is off the grids are referenced to ground and the output stage operates normally. If the LFO is on, its output signal is superimposed on the junction of the 680kΩ resistor and the two 270kΩ resistors. The bias voltage at the grids of the output tubes will then vary around 0V together with the LFO output signal, causing a change in the plate current and thus the output signal. Note that the impedance of the .02ufd coupling capacitors at the LFO output frequency is on the order of 1MΩ, and thus the LFO output signal will be attenuated only slightly by the voltage divider formed by the 270kΩ resistor and the .02ufd capacitor.

This approach can be dangerous. For example, if the LFO output coupling capacitor fails and a high DC voltage is fed to the junction of the 680kΩ resistor and the two 270kΩ resistors, the output stage becomes over-biased, which in turn can damage the output tubes, output transformer, and the power supply.

A better approach places a variable attenuator in series with the preamplifier signal. Either the series or the shunt element of the attenuator can be variable. Its resistance is controlled by the LFO output signal. A block diagram of a variable attenuator, where the shunt element is variable and the series element is fixed, is shown in Figure 3.19.

**Figure 3.19** Variable Attenuator

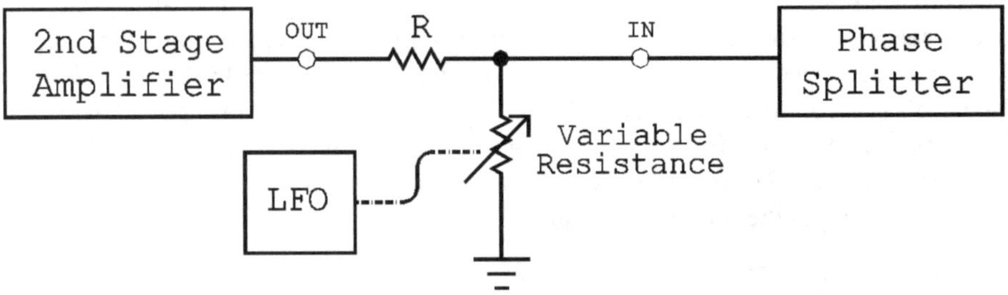


You can see from Figure 3.19 that the signal level at the junction of R and the variable resistance will vary as the resistance is varied. If the LFO output is used to vary the resistance, the signal level will vary together with the LFO output signal.

As usual, there are several ways you can implement the variable resistance in Figure 3.19. The most common approach is to use a *light-dependent resistor (LDR),* which is simply a device whose resistance varies when you shine light on it. The resistance is high when the device is dark, and lowers when it is exposed to light. The intensity of light required to lower the resistance and the minimum and maximum resistance values are properties of the device.

The LDR is packaged together with a light source, either in a plastic package or with the two devices mounted together in a piece of heat-shrink tubing. You use the LFO output to control the intensity of the light source, and the LDR as the variable resistance element in the attenuator.

Referring again to Figure 3.17, you can see that in the Fender circuit the second tube section is used to turn the light on and off, which in turn varies the resistance of the LDR. The stage operates like a voltage-controlled switch. With no signal at the grid, plate current causes a high voltage at the cathode, due to the 100kΩ cathode resistor, biasing the stage into cut-off. When the grid voltage is raised by the positive-going portion of the LFO output waveform, current flows in the plate, causing the voltage at the plate to drop. This provides enough voltage across the 100kΩ resistor in series with the light bulb to turn on the bulb. The 100kΩ resistor limits the current to prevent the light bulb from burning out. When the LFO waveform goes negative, the tube is biased into cut-off and plate current stops. So, during each positive-going section of the LFO waveform, the light turns on, and during each negative-going section it turns off.

One terminal of the LDR is grounded, and the other terminal is connected to the wiper of the tremolo intensity control. The intensity control is in turn connected between the output of the mixer stage, discussed in the section on reverberation, and ground. It shunts the output of the mixer stage to ground through the parallel combination of the control and the LDR. The contribution of the LDR to the shunt resistance is determined by the setting of the intensity control. If the intensity control is all the way up, the LDR will shunt the output of the mixer section to ground, providing the maximum tremolo effect. If the intensity control is all the way down, the LDR will have no effect on the mixer section output level.

## Effects Loops

In this section we discuss several approaches to adding effects loops to guitar amplifiers. As with reverberation and tremolo processors, solid-state designs can be a good choice in some situations, given that most external effects processors are solid-state. However, tube-based designs are also effective. We will restrict our discussion to passive and tube-based designs.

Every effects loop design must include an output to drive the effects processor input and an input to accept the effects processor output. The effects processor can be placed in series with the signal path, in which case the entire signal passes through the processor, or the effects loop can be implemented as a parallel side chain, in which case you mix the processed signal with the main path signal in the effects return circuit. Both approaches are shown in Figure 3.20.

**Figure 3.20** Effects Loop Topologies

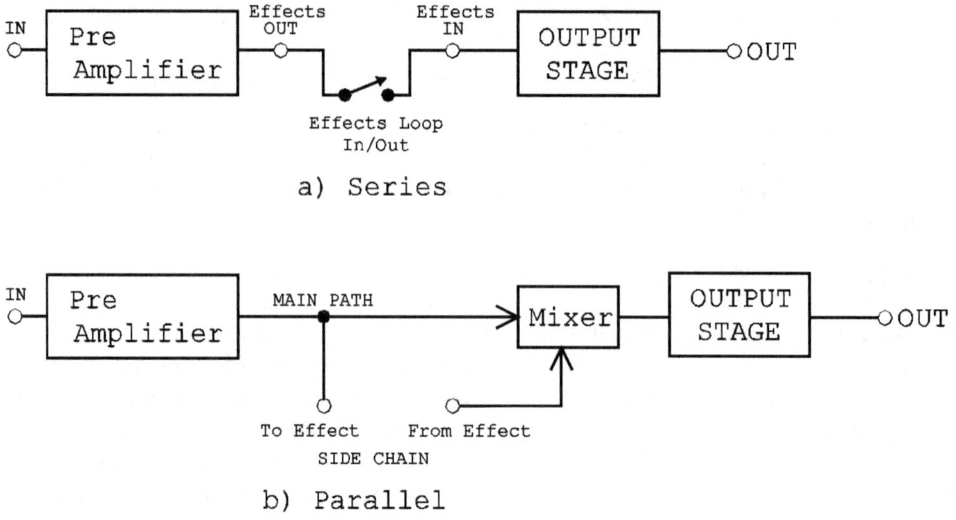


Many effects, including wah-wah, most distortion, delay, equalization, compression, chorus, and boost process the entire signal, so external processors implementing these effects are usually best placed in series with the signal path. The disadvantage to placing the effects processor in series is that the signal must always pass through the processor, even when no effects are desired. This can compromise the signal integrity, as explained earlier in this chapter.

Other effects, most notably reverberation, are best implemented in a parallel effects loop, since, as we have seen, the reverb signal is added to the dry signal to create the effect. The main path/side chain mixing can occur in the processor, in which case the processor can be in series with the signal with the resulting disadvantages, or in the amplifier, in which case signal integrity can be maintained in the main path.

**Figure 3.21** Figure 3.21 Passive Series Effects Loop

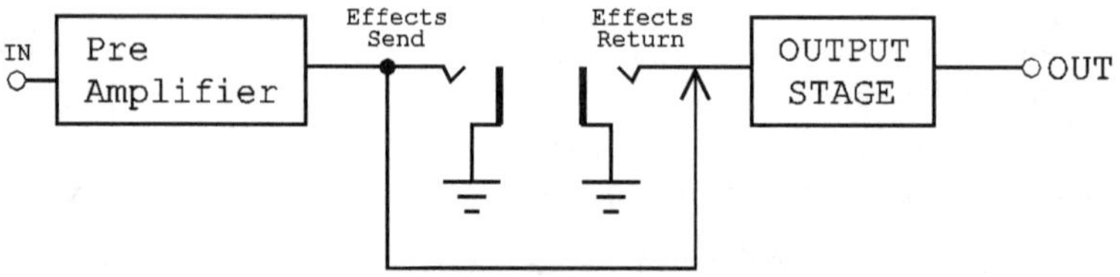


A simple series effects loop is shown in Figure 3.21. You add two phone jacks to break the signal path between the preamplifier output and the output stage input. For example, in the circuit of Figure 3.6, the effects send jack would be connected to the point labeled “output,” and the effects return jack would be connected to the input capacitor of the phase splitter ($C_1$ in Figure 2.23). The effects return uses a switching jack, with the wiper connected to the effects send signal.

If you plug into the effects send jack, you access the preamplifier output signal. If you plug into the effects return jack, you connect to the output stage and disconnect the preamplifier signal. If you don’t plug into the effects return jack, the preamplifier output signal remains connected to the output stage. In normal operation, you send the preamplifier output signal from the effects send jack to the external processor input, and you connect the external processor's output signal to the output stage using the effects return jack.

You can also use the effects send output to drive a separate power amplifier, and you can use the effects return jack to drive the output stage from an external source such as a separate preamplifier.

This circuit has several serious drawbacks that make it unsuitable for most applications:

— You can't adjust either the preamplifier output level or the output stage input level. While it is possible to add level controls, they affect the main signal path when you're not using the effects loop.

— The level and impedance of the preamplifier output signal may be unsuitable to drive the external processor input. Preamplifier output signal levels can easily reach tens of volts, and, as we discussed earlier in this chapter, external processor input buffer amplifiers often overload at these signal levels. Further, the preamplifier output impedance is quite high, usually around 45kΩ, which, depending on the input characteristics of the external processor, can cause frequency response or level errors.

— The external processor's output signal level may be inadequate to properly drive the output stage.

We will discuss solutions to these problems later in this section.

## *Passive Parallel Effects Loop*

If your amplifier has two independent channels, you can implement a passive parallel effects loop that avoids many of the problems of the passive series effects loop discussed above. Figure 3.22 shows the basic circuit.

**Figure 3.22** Passive Parallel Effects Loop for Two-Channel Amplifier

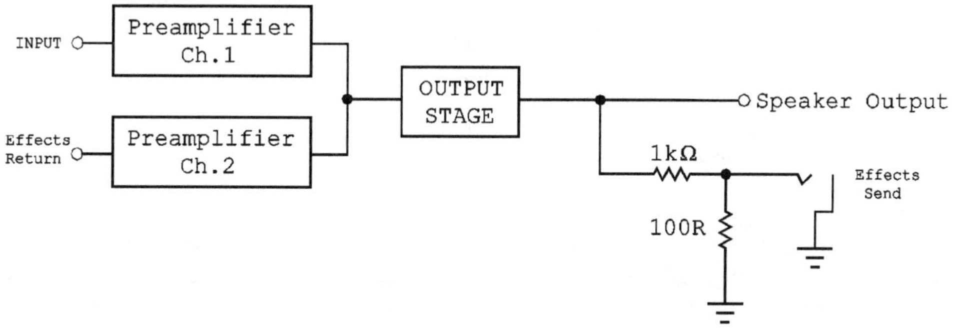


In this design you use the second channel as the effects return amplifier. As long as the output level of the effects processor is within the acceptable voltage range for the input amplifier (lower than about 1Vrms), this technique will work well.

The effects output is taken from the amplifier's speaker output. Since the signal level is quite high at the speaker output, a resistive attenuator is used to provide a suitable output level. Usually, around 20dB of attenuation is needed. The load presented by the attenuator to the output stage should be small compared to the speaker load, so we use 1kΩ and 100Ω resistors, as shown.

You can also obtain a signal from the second input jack of channel one. That is, you plug your guitar into input 1 of channel one and the input signal for the effects processor is taken from input 2 of channel one. The signal level will be quite low, and this technique can cause additional loading of the guitar output signal and lower overall amplifier gain, so you should listen carefully before choosing this approach. It's less risky if you have already buffered the guitar signal, for example by routing it through a pedal, before it reaches the amplifier's input.

While this design works well technically, it's only useful for effects that function properly in a parallel configuration. Most effects require a series configuration. However, you can use the attenuated speaker output for other useful purposes, including driving additional amplifiers and providing a direct signal for recording.

## *Buffered Series Effects Loop*

The best way to implement an effects loop is to buffer the effects send and return signals. Since most external effects are intended to be placed in series, we will limit our discussion to series loops. You can design a parallel effects loop; the main path is kept inside the amplifier, and the effects return amplifier output is fed to a mixer stage, where it is mixed with the main path signal, just as with the reverberation processor.

An effects send buffer using the cathode follower design of Figure 2.18 is shown in Figure 3.23.

**Figure 3.23** Effects Send Buffer

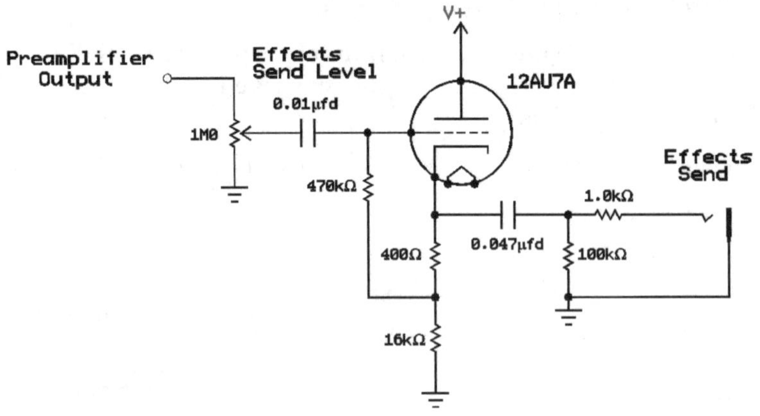


The preamplifier output is connected to the Effects Send Level control. The wiper of the control is connected to the grid of the cathode follower stage with a coupling capacitor. The cathode follower stage has very high input impedance, low output impedance, and a gain of slightly less than one, as described in Chapter 2. The output of the stage is coupled through a capacitor to the effects send jack. The 100kΩ resistor ensures that the output is referenced to ground, and the 1kΩ resistor protects the stage if the output is inadvertently grounded.

The output of the effects send buffer is thus a low-impedance, high-current version of the preamplifier output signal, with variable level, which is exactly what we need to drive an external effects processor.

The effects return buffer is a conventional gain stage. Figure 3.24 shows a gain stage implemented using the other half of the 12AU7A tube used for the effects send buffer.

**Figure 3.24** Effects Return Buffer

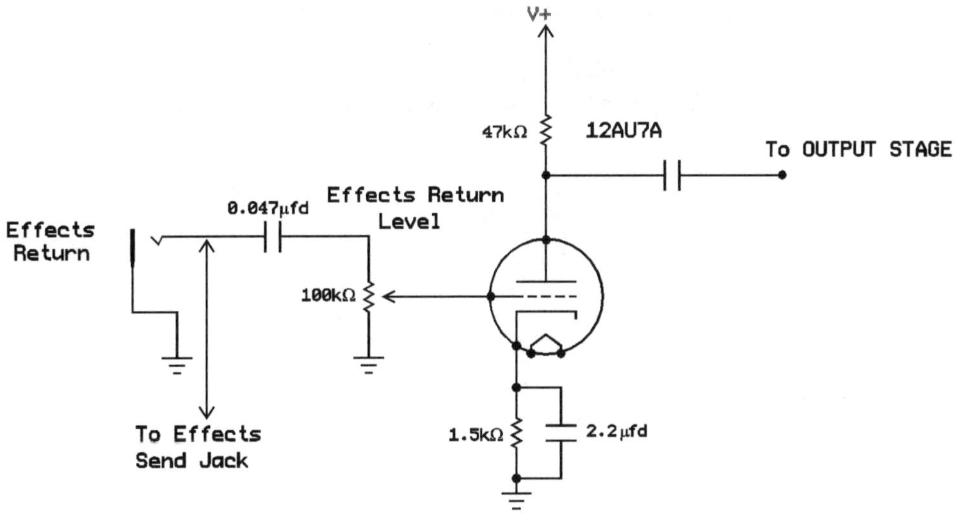


The external effects processor output is routed through a .047ufd capacitor to the 100kΩ Effects Level control. This network biases the grid to ground and isolates it from any DC voltage that may appear at the input. The gain of the stage is about 12, or 22dB. This is less gain than if we used a 12AX7A tube, but, since the external effects processor output level is fairly high, the gain provided should be sufficient.

If you use the effects loop buffers described in this section, the signal will always be routed through the two additional stages. This provides additional gain, and should result in little degradation of the signal. However, if the simplest signal path is desired when effects are not used, the effects loop can be bypassed, as shown in Figure 3.25.

**Figure 3.25** Effects Loop Bypass Switch

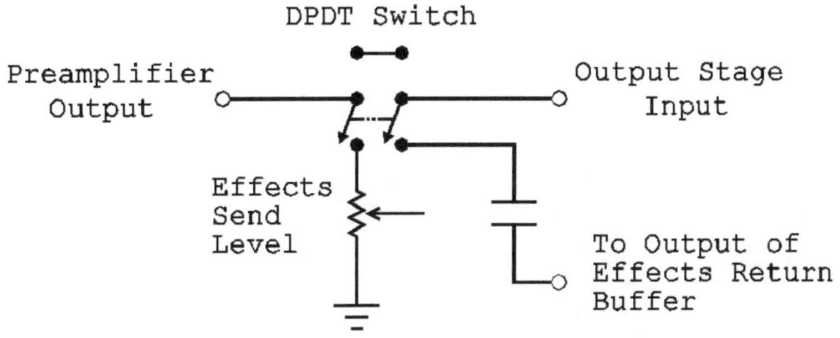


In the circuit of Figure 3.25, we use a *double-pole, double-throw (DPDT)* switch to bypass the effects loop buffers. The switch has two independent sections, each of which can connect the wiper of the switch to either of two poles. When the wipers are connected to the lower poles, as in Figure 3.25, the preamplifier output is connected to the effects send buffer by the left-hand section of the switch and the effects return buffer output is connected to the output stage by the right-hand section. When the wipers are connected to the upper poles, the preamplifier output is connected directly to the output stage, completely bypassing the effects loop circuitry.

You can implement the switching function using a DPDT switch or a DPDT relay. With a relay you can automatically engage the switch when an effect is selected. In either case care must be taken to avoid noises when switching. Special switches and relays can help prevent switching noise, as can proper circuit design. If you use the DPDT switch approach, you can avoid noise by switching the effects loop in or out as desired before turning on the amplifier.

# Chapter 4
# Amplifier Construction, Testing and Troubleshooting

Once you design your amplifier, you must procure all of the needed components and then assemble and test it. This chapter will describe the various components used in a tube amplifier, show how the components are mounted and connected together, and, finally, discuss the equipment and techniques used for testing and troubleshooting. You can find sources for components and test equipment in Appendix A.

## Electronic Components

### *Resistors and Potentiometers*

Fixed resistors are the most common components used in amplifiers. They are specified by their resistance (in ohms), the amount of power they can dissipate (in watts), their precision (in percent), and the material used in their construction. Resistors are made of metal and other films, carbon and ceramic composition, and are wire-wound. You will most often use ½ watt, 5% tolerance metal film resistors, with wire-wound resistors used in higher-wattage applications. The power rating of a resistor should be at least double the calculated power dissipated by the device in the circuit.

Typical resistors used in tube amplifiers are shown in Figure 4.1.

**Figure 4.1** Typical Resistors

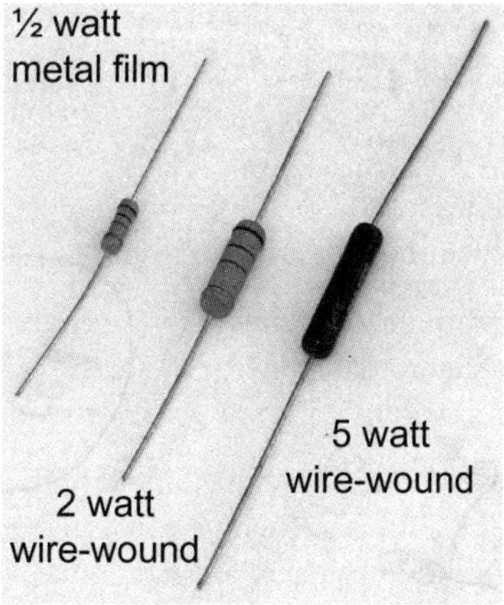


Lower-wattage resistors are marked with colored bands to identify their value and precision, as specified in the *standard electronic color code*. Four bands are normally used. The first two bands are the first two digits of the value, and the third band is the decimal multiplier. The fourth band is the tolerance. The colors and the numbers they represent are:

| | |
|---|---|
| Black | 0 |
| Brown | 1 |
| Red | 2 |
| Orange | 3 |
| Yellow | 4 |
| Green | 5 |
| Blue | 6 |
| Violet | 7 |
| Grey | 8 |
| White | 9 |
| No $4^{th}$ band | 20% tolerance |
| Silver $4^{th}$ band | 10% tolerance |
| Gold $4^{th}$ band | 5% tolerance |

So, for example, a 47kΩ, 5% tolerance resistor is marked yellow-violet-orange-gold. A 3.9kΩ, 10% tolerance resistor is marked orange-white-red-silver. The size of the resistor indicates its power rating. Higher-precision resistors are also available; they are normally marked with numbers rather than colored bands. Higher-wattage resistors can be marked either way.

A typical potentiometer is shown in Figure 4.2.

The value (in ohms) and the taper are written on the device. As explained in Chapter Two, potentiometers can have a linear taper, which is usually identified by the letter *B*, or a logarithmic taper, which is usually identified by the letter *A*. Potentiometers are available with various power ratings; tube amplifiers normally use ¼ watt or ½ watt units.

**Figure 4.2** Potentiometer ½ watt, ¼" Shaft, 3/8" Bushing, Solder Lugs

The mechanical attributes of a potentiometer are also important, including:

— The diameter and type of control shaft, which determines the type of knob that can be used. Many amplifiers use potentiometers with ¼" shafts; others use smaller units with 1/8" shafts. Shafts can be round, knurled, split, or half-round.

— The size of the bushing, which determines the diameter of the hole needed to mount the control. A potentiometer with a 1/4" shaft will use a 5/16" or 3/8" bushing, while a potentiometer with a 1/8" shaft will often use a ¼" bushing.

— The way you connect the potentiometer to the circuit. Hand-wired amplifiers normally use potentiometers with solder lugs, while amplifiers using *printed circuit boards (PCBs)* normally use PCB-mount potentiometers, which feature longer, straight pins to connect directly to the PCB traces.

## *Capacitors*

*Electrolytic* capacitors are polarized, that is, one lead of the capacitor must be held at a positive DC potential with respect to the other lead. They are specified by their value and their maximum operating voltage. For safety and reliability, the specified maximum voltage should comfortably exceed the actual circuit voltage. You can use 25V electrolytic capacitors in most cathode bypass applications.

Normally, the negative side of the capacitor is grounded and the positive side is connected to a positive DC voltage. However, in some cases, such as the bias supply, which is negative, the positive terminal of the filter capacitor is grounded. If you inadvertently connect an electrolytic capacitor backwards, it will fail at a voltage much lower than its rated voltage.

Most larger-value capacitors (1ufd and above) are electrolytic, including the power-supply filter capacitors and the cathode bypass capacitors used in tube amplifiers. Mechanically, electrolytic capacitors can have *axial* leads, where one lead is attached at each end of the device, or *radial* leads, where both leads are at one end. Older electrolytic capacitors were constructed in aluminum cans and chassis-mounted; each can often contained 2-4 capacitors with a common ground. Some can capacitors are available as replacement parts, but they cost much more than standard modern parts. You choose what type of capacitor to use based on the construction method used, as discussed later in this chapter. Figure 4.3 shows three typical electrolytic capacitors.

**Figure 4.3** Electrolytic Capacitors

Lower-value capacitors are *non-polarized,* that is, they can be connected either way in a circuit. Non-polarized capacitors are also specified by their value and maximum operating voltage. There are several types of non-polarized capacitors, but the two types most commonly used in tube amplifiers are *ceramic disk* capacitors for values below about 1nfd, and *polyester* or *polypropylene* capacitors, which are used for capacitances in the range of around 1nfd to .47ufd. Figure 4.4 shows typical non-polarized capacitors.

**Figure 4.4** Typical Non-Polarized Capacitors

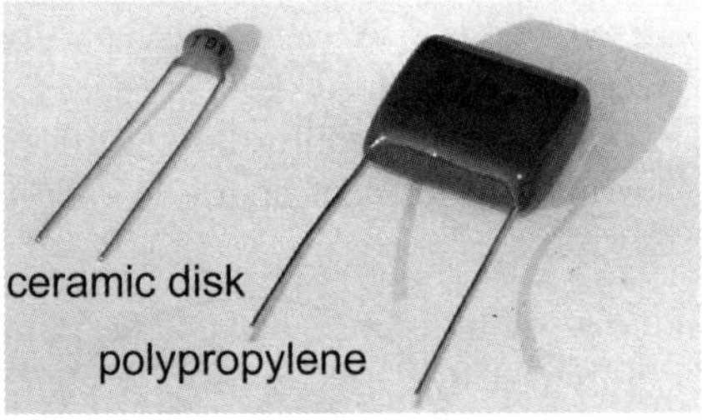


The maximum operating voltage of ceramic disk capacitors is usually around 1kV, which is plenty for tube amplifier applications. You should choose the specified voltage rating of polypropylene capacitors depending on where they will be used in the circuit. In most cases, the voltage rating should be comfortably higher than the supply voltage. Some older capacitors are marked using the electronic color code, but the value, voltage rating, and tolerance is written on nearly all modern devices.

## *Inductors*

Apart from chokes, discussed later in this chapter, most tube amplifiers do not use inductors due to their scarcity and high cost.

## *Diodes*

As discussed in Chapter 1, diodes have an anode and a cathode. The cathode is usually marked with a stripe on the device. Diodes are rated by *peak inverse voltage (PIV),* or the maximum positive voltage from cathode to anode the diode can withstand before failing, and maximum current that can flow from anode to cathode. Diodes used in tube amplifiers have a specified PIV rating of around 1000V, and can handle 1-3A of current. A typical diode is shown in Figure 4.5.

**Figure 4.5** FR307 Diode, 1kV PIV, 3A

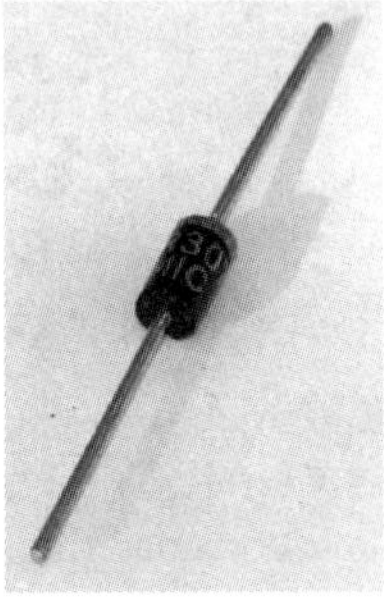

## *Transformers and Chokes*

Power transformers are specified by the voltage and maximum current of each of the secondary windings. All power transformers have a 6.3V secondary winding to power the tube filaments, unless a separate filament supply transformer is used. It may or may not be center-tapped. If a center tap is provided, you normally ground it to keep the DC potential of the winding close to ground. If a center tap is not provided, you can connect 100Ω resistors from each end of the winding to ground for the same purpose. The maximum current available should be comfortably higher than the sum of all the specified filament currents for the tubes used. For example, if you design an amplifier with three 12AX7A preamplifier tubes and two 6CA7 output tubes, the total specified filament current will be 3 x 0.3 A + 2 x 1.5 A = 3.9 A. The transformer secondary specification should then be around 5A at 6.3V.

A high-voltage secondary winding is also needed to provide the supply voltage. The most common configuration used is a center-tapped winding, where the center tap is grounded and each end is connected to a diode or a string of diodes. The output voltage is specified from each end of the secondary to the center tap, for example, 345-0-345$V_{rms}$. Because the specified voltage is rms, the peak voltage is 483V, and the voltage at the first filter capacitor with no load is almost 483V as well. However, when you draw current from the secondary the voltage will drop some due to resistance in the winding and voltage drop across the diodes, so the actual maximum voltage under load from a secondary is around 130% of the specified rms value, or 450V in this case.

You determine the specified maximum current of the high-voltage secondary by adding up the currents used in each section of the amplifier. In most cases, the majority of the current will be used by the output tubes. If the output stage is Class A, the total current flowing in the plates of the output tubes is the sum of the quiescent currents. If the output stage is Class AB, the maximum current can be determined from the load line. For example, referring to Figure 2.31 you can see that the quiescent current is around 68mA in each tube, or 136mA total. The maximum current in each tube can reach around 120mA, but when this occurs there is little or no current in the other tube, so you can estimate the maximum current in the output tubes is around 140mA. You can add an additional 10% or so for screen grid current, and another 10-20mA for the rest of the stages in a basic design, for a total in this case of around 175mA. So, to allow some margin, a secondary rated at 200–250mA would be adequate for this application.

Power transformers intended for use with tube rectifiers must provide a third secondary to power the filament of the rectifier tube. The rectifier tube's filament is at a DC potential equal to the supply voltage, so it can not be powered by the same filament supply as the rest of the tubes. Most common rectifier tubes specify a filament supply voltage of 5V. The specified maximum secondary current must be adequate to comfortably supply the rectifier tube used. For example, the 5Y4GT rectifier specifies a filament voltage of 5V and a filament current of 2A.

Many power transformers provide two primary windings, which are connected in parallel for 120VAC operation and in series for 220VAC operation.

Chokes are specified by their inductance, maximum current, and maximum voltage. For most power supply applications, inductance should be between 4 and 10 Henries as discussed in Chapter 2. The maximum current depends on the circuit, but in most PP tube amplifier power supplies the plate current is taken from the first filter capacitor, so only the screen grid current and the current for the preamplifier tubes flows through the choke. In the previous example of an amplifier using three 12AX7A preamplifier tubes and two EL-34 output tubes, this is around 20-30mA, so a choke with a specified maximum current of 40-50mA would be adequate in that application. In SE amplifiers all of the supply current normally flows through the choke, so its current rating must be higher. The maximum voltage rating should be comfortably higher than the supply voltage.

Output transformers are specified by primary winding impedance and configuration, secondary winding impedances, power handling capability, and bandwidth, or frequency response. Primary windings for PP output transformers are center-tapped. Some have additional taps intended to be connected to the screen grids to achieve what is called ultra-linear operation, although they are rarely used in guitar amplifiers. Primary windings for SE output are not center-tapped. Secondary windings are usually, but not always, designed for 4Ω, 8Ω, and 16Ω output impedances.

Power handling capability and bandwidth are related. As power increases, bandwidth decreases, so an output transformer has a specified frequency response at a specified power output. If you decrease the power output the bandwidth increases, and if you increase the power output the bandwidth decreases. This relationship is important for guitar amplifiers, because the bandwidth needed to reproduce a guitar signal is significantly less than the bandwidth needed for most other audio applications. As explained in Chapter 2, the low E on a guitar is around 84Hz, and the highest harmonic of significance is well below 10kHz. So, an output transformer designed to accurately reproduce a guitar signal at a given power can be smaller and less expensive than an output transformer designed to accurately reproduce a 20-20kHz audio signal at the same power. On the other hand, a 50 watt output transformer from a guitar amplifier will not provide full bandwidth at 50 watts in an audio amplifier. Again, when specifying an output transformer for a guitar amplifier, look for a unit that has adequate power handling capability over the bandwidth of interest. Often, a full-bandwidth output transformer intended for use at a given output level in audio applications can be used at a higher power output level in a guitar amplifier.

Transformers can be mounted either horizontally or vertically. Horizontally means that the core laminations of the transformer are horizontal, while vertically means that the core laminations are vertical. Figure 4.6 shows the top of a typical amplifier chassis, with the power transformer mounted horizontally, the choke and output transformer mounted vertically, and sockets for three preamplifier tubes and two output tubes. Note the locations and orientations of the power transformer, choke, and output transformer, which have been chosen to minimize hum in the preamplifier circuit and magnetic coupling between the transformers and choke.

**Figure 4.6** Typical Chassis Layout

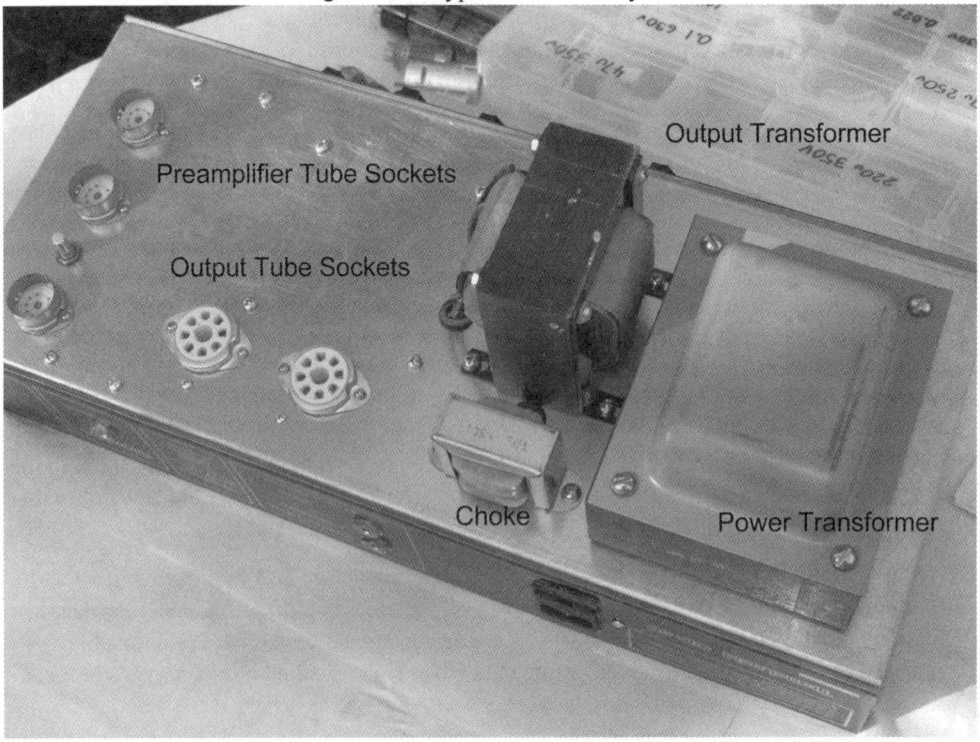

Some tube amplifiers use transformers in other parts of the circuit, including at the input of microphone preamplifiers and to couple between various stages. However, you rarely see this in guitar amplifiers.

## *Tubes*

There are thousands of different tubes available, and many are suitable for use in guitar amplifiers. Some tubes manufactured in the United States are referred to by one designation, while equivalent tubes manufactured in Europe are referred to by a different designation. *Industrial Type* tubes with equivalent performance also have different designators, as do tubes manufactured for military use.

Most guitar amplifiers use the 12A_7 series of tubes for the preamplifier and phase splitter stages. The 12A_7 tubes, a sample of which is shown in Figure 4.7, are called *miniature* tubes, and utilize a 9-pin miniature socket.

**Figure 4.7** 12AX7A Tube

Five different output tubes are used in most guitar amplifiers. The 6BQ5 is a miniature 9-pin pentode tube used in lower-power output stages. All of the other output tubes are larger and use an *octal* socket. The 6V6 is used in lower-power output stages, the 6L6GC and 6CA7 are used in medium-power output stages, and the 6550 is used in high-power output stages. In all cases, multiple tubes can be used in parallel, as described in Chapter 2, to increase output power. Samples of the five output tubes are shown in Figure 4.8.

**Figure 4.8** Output Tubes

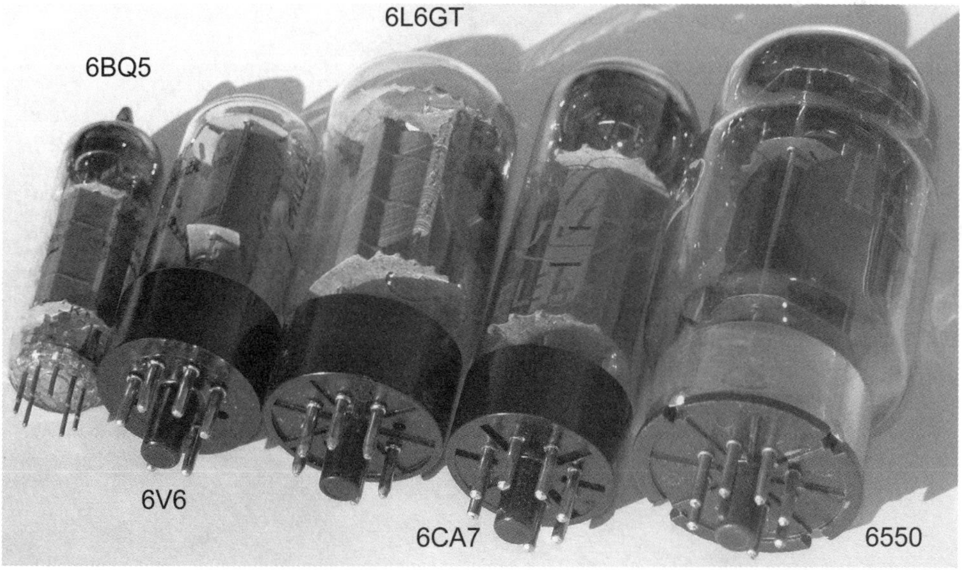

Two different rectifier tubes are used in most guitar amplifiers. The 5Y3GT is used in lower-power amplifiers, and the 5AR4 is used in higher-power amplifiers. Both use octal sockets. Samples of the two rectifier tubes are shown in Figure 4.9.

**Figure 4.9** Rectifier Tubes

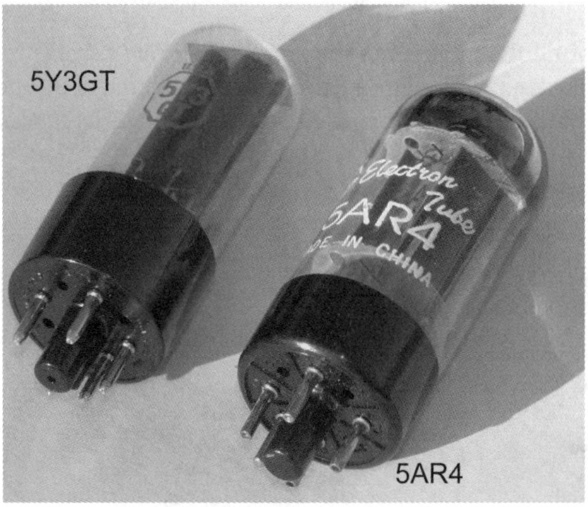


You can find performance data, alternate designations and pin-outs for these tubes in Appendix B.

## *Spring Reverb Tanks*

Typical spring reverb tanks are shown in Figure 4.10. In addition to providing different input and output impedances, spring reverb tanks are available in long or short configurations, and with different numbers of springs. Long tanks provide longer reverberation times and deeper reverberation, while short tanks are less expensive and can fit in smaller enclosures. Using multiple springs with different characteristics provides a richer, more complex output signal. You should use the tank that sounds best and meets the mechanical and electrical design requirements.

## *Choosing Electronic Components*

Real-world electronic components are not perfect. That is, resistors are not purely resistive; they also have inductance and capacitance. Inductors have resistance and capacitance, and capacitors have inductance and resistance. Components made of different materials have more or less of these *parasitic* properties. Furthermore, component tolerances can cause identically labeled components to have different values, and tubes of the same type can have quite different properties, as discussed previously. Finally, these properties can change over time and they can also change dynamically, that is, with the current or voltage applied to the device. All of these factors can affect the sound of an amplifier.

**Figure 4.10** Spring Reverb Tanks

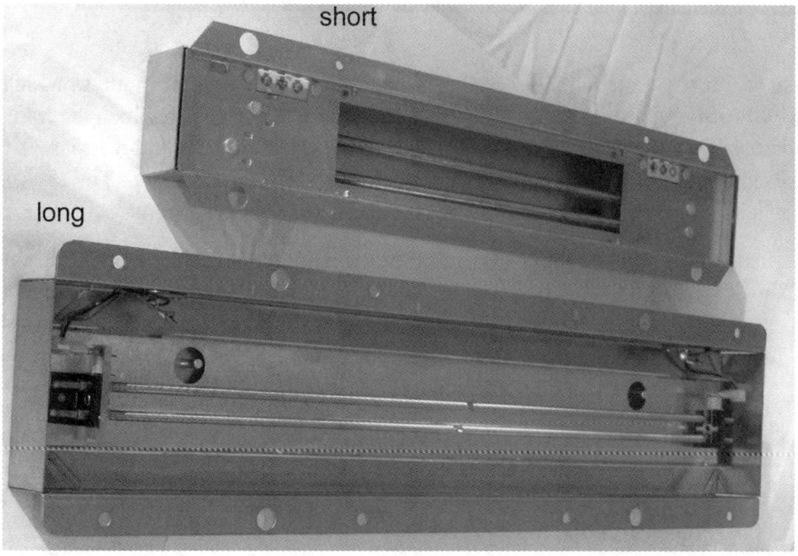


Modern resistors and polystyrene capacitors have very low parasitic properties, and are quite stable with respect to time, temperature, and dynamic current and voltage. High-quality transformers also have low parasitic properties and good consistency. You can select tubes when necessary, for example, for low noise or for matched parameters when used in PP output stages. Amplifiers constructed with modern components will generally perform as designed and, if multiple units are constructed, their performance will be consistent.

Older "vintage" components, such as carbon composition resistors and oil and paper capacitors, can have greater parasitic properties, wider tolerances, and be more prone to failure and variability due to age and dynamics. Some designers prefer these components because they believe that their amplifiers sound better with them. This is not because the component is more perfect, but rather because its imperfections make the amplifier, in the opinion of the designer or user, sound better. If you want to use these kinds of components, for example to repair or recreate a classic amplifier, you must perform careful testing and extensive listening to determine their effect on the overall sound.

You should not reuse electrolytic capacitors, because the electrolyte dries out over time, causing leakage currents that can increase ripple and cause the capacitor to fail. You should check any other reused capacitors subject to high voltages, such as coupling capacitors, by measuring their capacitance and measuring the DC voltage at both ends when powered up to make sure that no DC voltage is leaking through.

## Mechanical Components

### *Chassis*

The chassis is a formed metal enclosure, usually made of steel or aluminum, to which you attach all of the other components. The chassis includes a top panel, to which the transformers, tubes, and possibly other components are usually mounted, and front and rear panels, to which the controls and input, output, and power connectors are usually mounted. The chassis is then mounted in a cabinet, which may or may not include speakers, to form the complete amplifier.

There are many variations on chassis design. Some manufacturers, like Fender, mount the chassis upside-down, with the tubes and transformers hanging from the bottom. Others, like Marshall, mount the chassis upright. Still other designs place the front panel on top of the amplifier, with the tubes hanging from the rear panel and the transformers on the top panel. Ultimately, the chassis design is determined by the cabinet.

A typical chassis is shown in Figure 4.11. This chassis is designed to be mounted upside-down, with the input and controls mounted on a sloped front panel, and the outputs and power connector mounted on the rear panel. Threaded inserts are included to allow the chassis to be mounted to the cabinet from the top.

**Figure 4.11** Typical Chassis

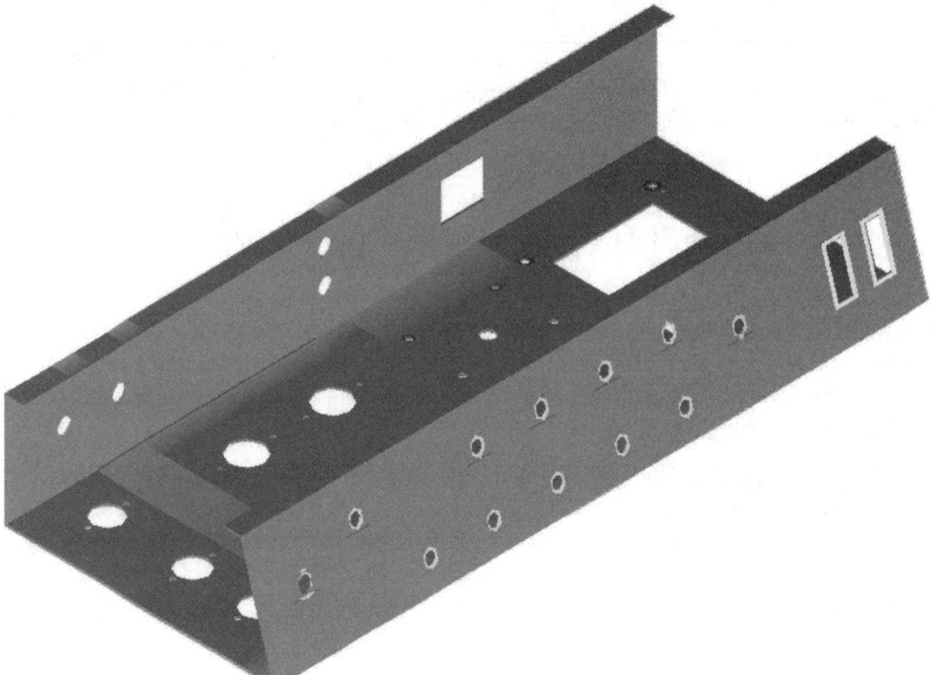

## Tube Sockets

Tubes are physically mounted on the chassis and electrically connected to the rest of the circuitry using sockets. Sockets are made from ceramic or phenolic material, and can be mounted from the top or bottom of the chassis. Connections are made either using solder lugs on the sockets, or the socket is mounted directly to a PCB, as discussed in the next section. Sockets for preamplifier tubes are often shielded, and sockets for output tubes often include a means to physically secure the tube in the socket, particularly when the tubes are mounted upside-down. Typical ceramic tube sockets are shown in Figure 4.12.

**Figure 4.12** Typical Ceramic Tube Socket

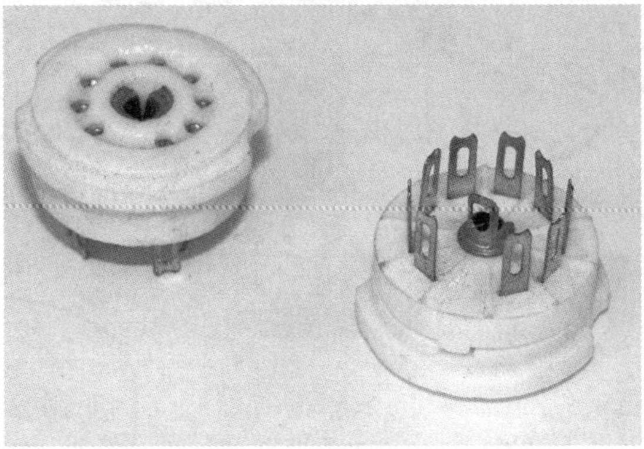

## Component Connection

You can connect the components in a guitar amplifier in several ways. Some components, such as the tube sockets discussed in the previous section, have solder lugs to which you can directly connect components. However, many components require some kind of hardware for physically mounting the component and making electrical connections from the component to other components.

Modern mass-produced amplifiers often use PCBs, which are made of an insulating material and have copper traces etched on one or both surfaces. You drill holes in the board at the proper places and mount the components, which are interconnected by the copper traces. Connections to components not mounted on the PCB, such as transformers, controls, and switches, are made using various wiring schemes. A typical PCB with components on top and copper traces on the bottom is shown in Figure 4.13.

For prototyping and smaller production runs, PCBs can be impractical because of the time and expense associated with their design and manufacture. In addition, some designers avoid PCBs to imitate as closely as possible the construction techniques used in classic amplifiers.

The connections in amplifiers without PCBs are made using *point-to-point* wiring, where components are interconnected using only wire. These amplifiers also require a means to mechanically mount the components, and you can use any of several systems to do so.

**Figure 4.13** Typical PCB

*Terminal strips,* shown in Figure 4.14, are available in a variety of sizes. You fasten the terminal strips to the chassis and mount the components to the lugs. Each lug can accommodate a number of component leads and wires. You can see from Figure 4.13 that some of the lugs are used to fasten the terminal strip to the chassis and are thus grounded. You can use these lugs to make connections to ground but, as discussed later in this chapter, you need to use proper grounding techniques. Terminal strips are inexpensive and flexible, and are useful even in designs that use other connection schemes.

**Figure 4.14** Terminal Strips

*Turret boards* were used before the advent of PCBs in military and other high-reliability applications. As you can see in Figure 4.15, turrets are fastened to a rigid, insulating board, and components and connecting wires are wrapped around and soldered to the turrets. You can either use customized turret boards for a particular design, or prefabricated boards with rows of turrets on each side. The boards are mounted to the chassis using *stand-offs,* which are internally threaded metal or nylon posts of varying sizes.

**Figure 4.15** Turret Board

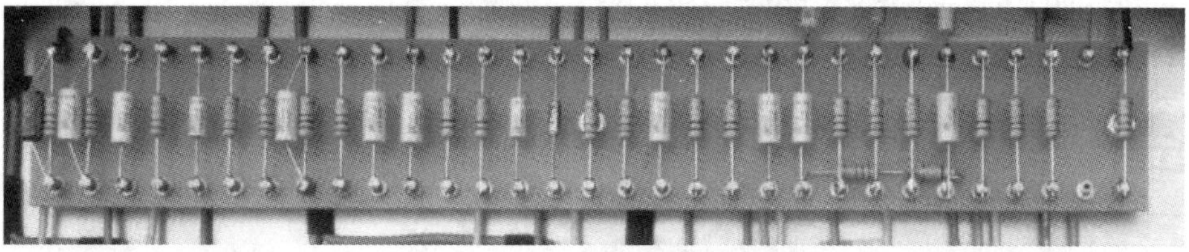

*Eyelet board* is similar to turret board, except eyelets are inserted in the board instead of turrets. Component leads are inserted in and soldered to the eyelets. In older Fender amplifiers, the board is flexible, and a second layer is added under the eyelet board to insulate the circuitry. The whole assembly is then fastened to the chassis. An example of an eyelet board is shown in Figure 4.16.

**Figure 4.16** Eyelet Board

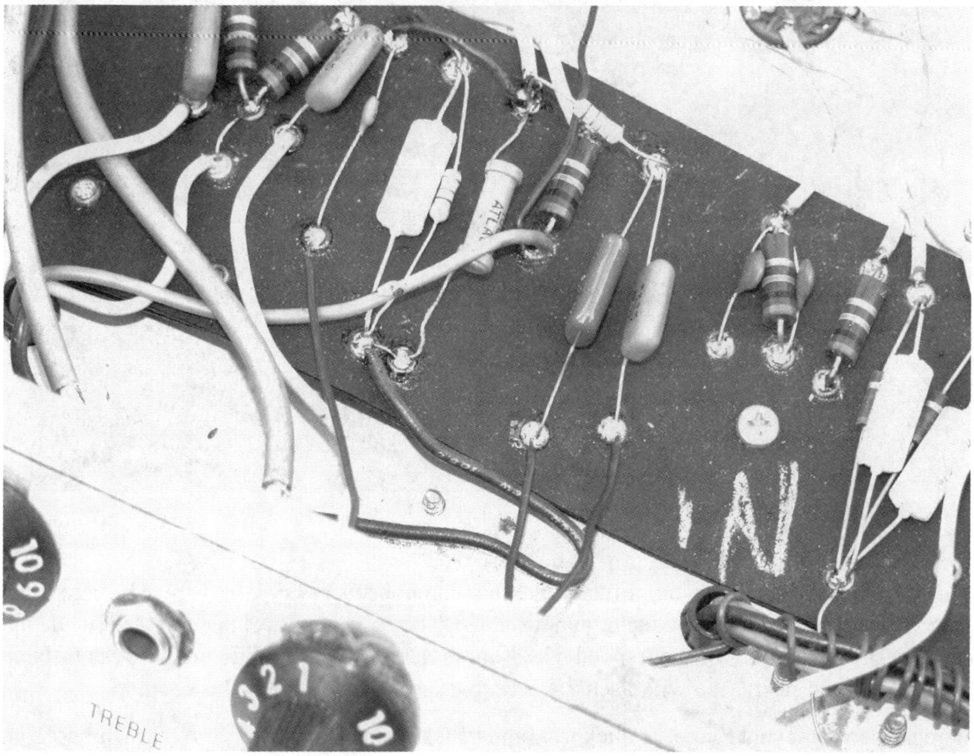


*Prototype boards* are made by a number of manufacturers. Basic prototyping systems include an insulated board predrilled in a grid pattern, often with holes spaced at 0.1" intervals. Some boards include copper traces to use in interconnections. A variety of metal pins are available, which you stick in the holes where needed. You then connect components and wires to the pins. The boards are mounted to the chassis using stand-offs. A typical prototype board with pins is shown in Figure 4.17.

The connection system you choose depends on the complexity of the circuit and the number of amplifiers you intend to make. Simple circuits can often be constructed using only terminal strips. You should consider a combination of terminal strips and prototype boards for more complex circuits made in single or small quantities. Mass-produced designs use PCBs or custom turret or eyelet boards. If you intend to modify an existing amplifier, it's often easiest to use the existing connection system, assuming it is in good condition.

**Figure 4.17** Prototype Board

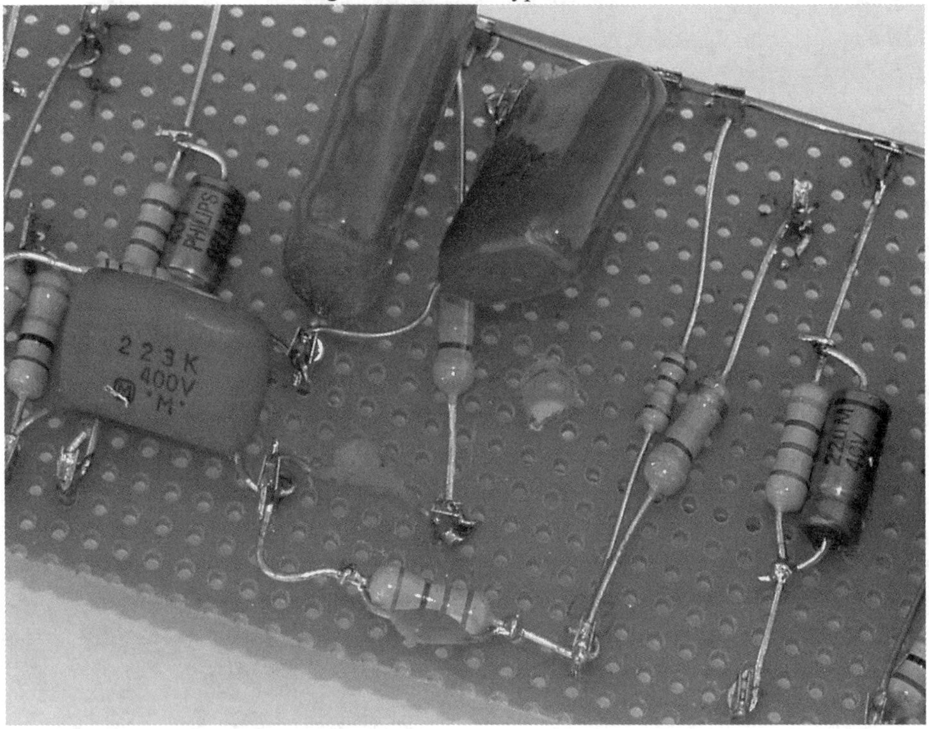


## *Wire*

You make connections in an amplifier with either components or hook-up wire. The wire used in most instances is single-conductor and insulated. The conductor is either stranded (made up of many small wires) or solid. Stranded wire is more flexible, while solid-core wire can be bent and routed more easily. We will discuss where to use each type later in this chapter.

Wire is specified by its gauge, or thickness, and its insulation resistance. Hook-up wire used in guitar amplifiers is usually 20 or 22 gauge, with an insulation resistance of at least 600 VDC. You can use different colored wire for different parts of the circuit to facilitate troubleshooting. For example, all ground wires can be green, all power supply wires red, and so on.

Some critical connections may require that you use *shielded* wire, which consists of one or more conductors surrounded by a wire shield. The shield is connected to ground at one or both ends. Connections that may require shielded wire include the wire from the input jack to the grid of the input stage tube and other wires that carry low-level signals close to sources of hum such as the power supply.

## *Input and Output Connectors*

The guitar input and speaker output connectors are usually ¼" *phone jacks.* A typical phone jack is shown in Figure 4.18. Note the ground connection, which contacts the barrel of the phone plug, and the signal (or *hot)* connection, which contacts the tip of the phone plug. The third connection is a switch. When there is no plug inserted in the jack, it is connected to the hot connection, and when a plug is inserted, the connection is broken. Uses for this switch are discussed in Chapter 2.

Phone jacks are also used for footswitches. If only one footswitch is needed, you can use a jack similar to those already discussed. If you need two switches, you can use a *stereo* phone jack, as shown in Figure 4.18. Other more elaborate phone jack switching schemes are also used in some designs.

Spring reverb tanks and some footswitches use *RCA jacks* for connection. You can see the RCA jacks mounted on the larger tank in Figure 4.10. A typical RCA plug is shown in Figure 4.18.

**Figure 4.18** Connectors

In some amplifiers the AC power cable is routed directly through a hole in the chassis using a plastic strain reliever to fix and insulate the cable. Other designs use an AC connector, often including a fuse holder, attached to the chassis and a standard detachable power cord. A typical AC connector is shown in Figure 4.19.

**Figure 4.19** AC Connector with fuse holder

**IMPORTANT:** FOR SAFETY, YOU MUST USE A GROUNDED AC POWER CORD, WITH THE GROUND WIRE SECURELY CONNECTED DIRECTLY TO THE CHASSIS NEAR WHERE THE AC ENTERS THE AMPLIFIER. IF YOU REPAIR OR MODIFY OLD AMPLIFIERS, YOU MUST REPLACE EXISTING 2-WIRE AC CORDS WITH GROUNDED CORDS.

## *Switching*

Mechanical switches are used to switch the amplifier on and off, to switch to the standby mode, and for footswitches. The on/off and standby switches can be *toggle* or *rocker* switches, and should be rated for at least 5A at 250VAC. Footswitches are usually *pushbutton* switches, and the currents and voltages switched are generally small. However, footswitches must be very strong mechanically, so normally larger, higher-rated switches are used.

Standby switches should be placed after the first filter capacitor of the power supply, as shown in Figs. 2.31 and 2.33. Otherwise, a large current will flow when the switch is thrown, which can cause switch failure.

Switches are specified by the number of *poles,* each pole representing an independent switch. For example, a *single-pole (SP)* switch contains one set of poles and thus can perform one switching function. A *double-pole (DP)* switch has two separate switches controlled by single actuator. Also, a switch can be *single-throw (ST)* or *double-throw (DT).* A ST switch has two connections. When the switch is on they are shorted and when the switch is off they are open. A DT switch has three connections. When the switch is in one position one of the connections is shorted to the second connection and open to the third connection. When the switch is in the other position the connection is open to the second connection and shorted to the third connection. So, for example, a SPST switch has two connections and one switching function, while a DPDT switch has a total of six connections and two independent switching functions. Schematic diagrams for various types of switches are shown in Figure 4.20.

**Figure 4.20** Switch Schematic Diagrams

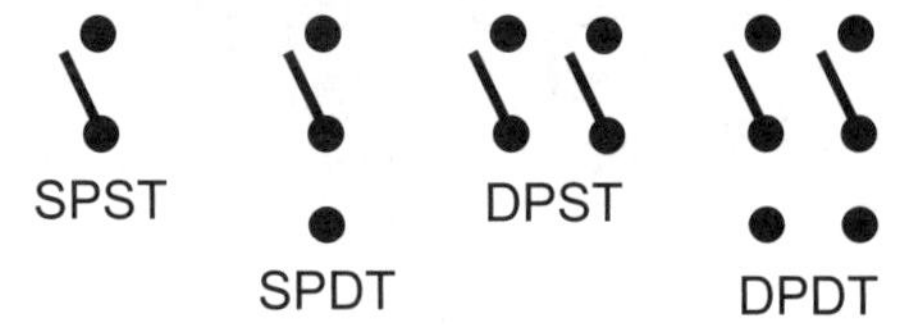


Typical power, standby, and foot switches are shown in Figure 4.21.

**Figure 4.21** Typical Switches

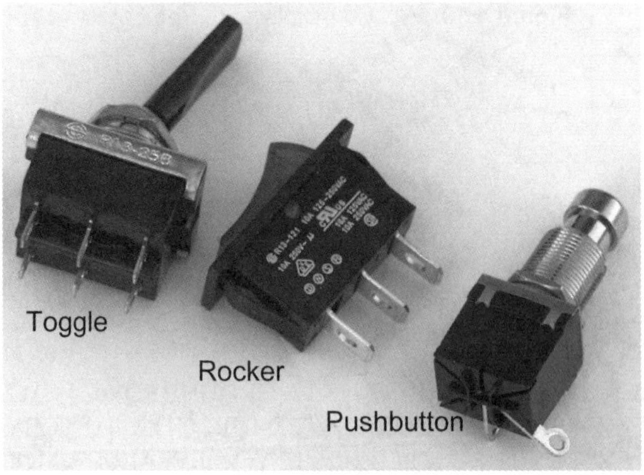

You can also actuate switching functions electrically. The most straightforward approach is to use a relay, as discussed in Chapter 3. Relays are inexpensive and available in a variety of forms, switching schemes, and actuating voltages. Normally, the actuating voltage is switched on and off by a footswitch, causing the relay to switch on and off. A separate power supply voltage is usually required. A typical relay is shown in Figure 4.22.

**Figure 4.22** DPDT Relay

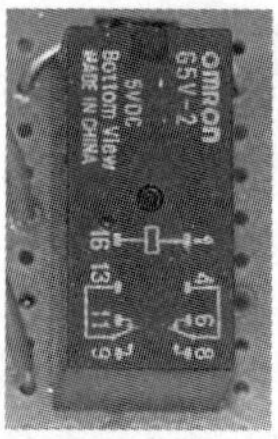


You can also electrically switch signals using semiconductor devices, such as *field-effect transistors (FETs)*. A detailed discussion of semiconductor-based switching schemes can be found, among other places, in the O'Conner references in the bibliography.

## *Indicators*

Indicators are used to show when an amplifier is on, in the standby mode, or in other modes such as overdrive. A variety of indicators are used in amplifiers, including *light-emitting diodes (LEDs)* and light bulbs. Older amplifiers often use a light bulb mounted in a panel-mounted socket, powered from the filament supply. Newer amplifiers use neon bulbs powered from the AC supply or LEDs. Some switches, such as the rocker switch shown in Figure 4.21, include an integrated neon light bulb with a series current-limiting resistor that can be used as a power or standby indicator. Typical indicators are shown in Figure 4.23.

**Figure 4.23** Typical Indicators

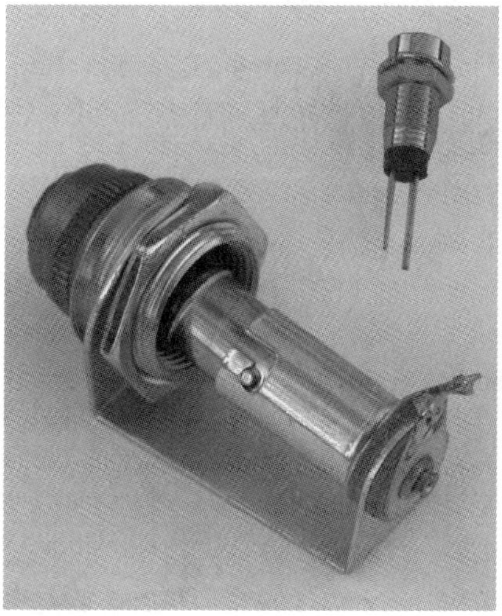

## *Fuses and Holders*

You must always include a fuse in series with the power transformer primary. Some amplifiers also fuse the DC supply voltage and the filament supply to further protect the power transformer and other components. Many amplifiers use either type 3AG fuses, which are 1.25" long and 0.25" in diameter, or type 2AG fuses, which are 0.57" long and 0.177" in diameter. Fuses are *fast-* or *slow-acting*. Fast-acting fuses will blow quickly when the current exceeds the specified value, while slow-acting fuses require the current to exceed the specified value for a longer time before blowing. Slow-acting fuses are generally used in the primary of the power transformer, usually rated from 1-4A, depending on the output power of the amplifier.

You can buy fuses with leads attached and connect them in the circuit as you would any other component, or you can mount the fuse in a fuse holder. Most older amplifiers use a panel-mounted 3AG fuse holder, as shown in Figure 4.24. Modern designs use panel-mounted fuse holders, holders integrated into the AC connector, as shown in Figure 4.19, or internal fuse clips, as shown in Figure 4.24.

**Figure 4.24** 3AG Fuse and Holders

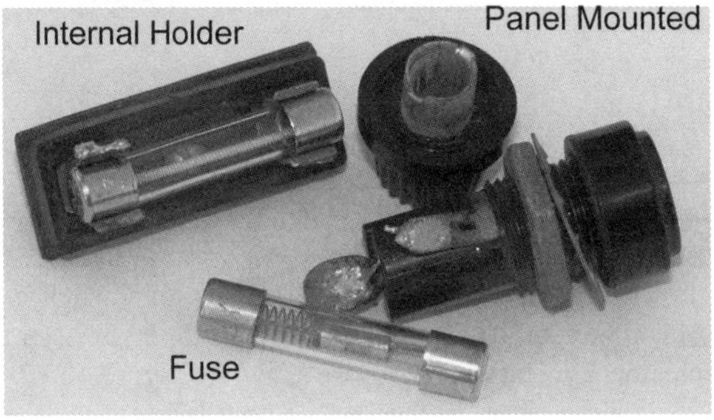


## *Control Panels*

You usually mount controls and connectors on the front and rear panels. The panels must be labeled somehow to identify the controls' and connectors' functions. While crude hand-written labeling may be acceptable for prototype units, you can label panels more professionally in several ways:

— Paint the panel and apply contrasting rub-on letters, and then apply clear lacquer over the letters. This approach is easy and inexpensive, but it is difficult to achieve consistent results.

— Create labels using a computer, and then print the labels on adhesive-backed paper or glue the label to the chassis. This approach works well, especially when the label is then covered with a thin sheet of clear plastic. You can also glue the label to the plastic sheet. Creating the labels requires skill in computer-aided design, and the labels and plastic cover must be drilled and formed to accept the controls and connectors.

— Create a silkscreen and paint the labels on the chassis or on thin sheets of aluminum that form the panels. This approach gives good results, but is only practical if you intend to make multiple units.

— Create the labels using a computer, and then send the file to a fabricator. Fabricators can engrave the labels on bi-laminate plastic or silkscreen or use a photoengraving process to create thin metal panels. The process is expensive, but results in high-quality panels.

— Create the labels using a computer, and then print the labels on special decal transfer paper (available from vendors such as www.lazertran.com), then apply the decals to the chassis.

Some amplifier builders modify existing amplifiers. If you take this approach, you may be able to reuse the existing panels and avoid the time and expense associated with creating new ones.

## Hardware

You use roundhead machine screws with nuts and lock washers to fasten most of the mechanical components to the chassis. Tube sockets, terminal strips and standoffs usually require #4 or #6 screws, while heavier items like transformers and chokes use #8 or #10 screws. The length depends on what is being fastened, but most screws are ½"–¾".

You can use *lug washers* to provide a chassis grounding point, and rubber *grommets* to protect wires running through the chassis. Standoffs made of nylon or aluminum are available in a variety of lengths and to fit a variety of screw sizes. 1" standoffs with 6-32 internal threads are a good choice for many applications.

As you will learn in the next section, special fiber insulating washers may be required for the input jack to prevent a ground loop. These washers have two parts, one of which is mounted inside the chassis and the other of which is mounted on the front panel. Typical lug washers, grommets, standoffs and insulating washers are shown in Figure 4.25.

**Figure 4.25** Hardware

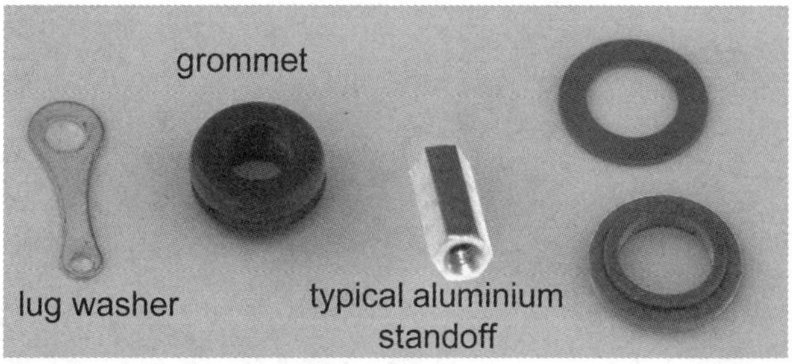


Potentiometers, switches and jacks are supplied with mounting hardware. Separate panels are usually held in place by the components mounted to the panel.

Some amplifiers use special hardware to mount the chassis to the cabinet. For example, Fender amplifiers have four long screws that extend through a metal strap at the top of the cabinet through the chassis via special channels; nuts and lock washers are applied to the end of the screw extending out of the bottom of the chassis. Some Ampeg amplifiers use a shock-mounting system, where the chassis connects to a panel on each side with rubber bushings, and then the panel is screwed to the cabinet. Other chasses have threaded inserts mounted in flanges, and mounting screws go through the cabinet and are screwed into the inserts. Most use flathead screws with cup washers or metal straps to support the screws. When you design your chassis, make sure that you accommodate attaching the chassis to the cabinet.

You can find a wide variety of knobs in the sources mentioned in Appendix A. Knobs must fit the potentiometer shafts they are intended to be used with, and should have a size, shape and markings compatible with the panel design used.

## Chassis Layout

The primary issues associated with component placement are:

— **Ergonomics:** The placement of the controls, jacks, and switches, particularly on the front panel, must be convenient and easy to understand.

— **Cooling:** The tubes should be located where they will receive adequate cooling. This is especially true for the output tubes, which generate the most heat. Many output tubes have a minimum specified distance between tubes to ensure adequate cooling. Forced-air cooling is used in some high-power amplifiers.

— **Hum:** Magnetic fields, particularly from power supply components, can induce hum in high-sensitivity circuitry such as the input amplifier. For this reason, the power supply is normally positioned as far away from the preamplifier stages as possible. In addition, you should orient the power transformer, choke, and output transformer to minimize induced currents in the coils of neighboring devices. One such orientation is shown in Figure 4.6. Note that the coils of the power transformer, output transformer, and choke are on different axes, which minimizes cross-coupling of magnetic fields and resulting induced hum.

— **Stability:** You should locate components as close to their associated circuitry as possible, and keep connecting wires as short as possible. This will help prevent oscillation by reducing parasitic capacitance and signal cross-coupling in the wiring. You must always locate grid stop resistors directly adjacent to the associated tube socket.

You can see a typical layout for the top of an amplifier in Figure 4.6, and a typical internal layout in Figure 4.26.

**Figure 4.26** Typical Internal Chassis Layout

Spring reverb tank springs can couple to the amplifier output through either vibrations in the enclosure or sound waves generated by the speaker. This coupling can cause feedback when the reverb is turned up. Further, the tank's transducers or wiring can pick up electro-magnetic fields, introducing hum and noise into the reverb tank output signal. This problem is mitigated somewhat by the shielding provided by the tank enclosure and the use of shielded wire to connect the tank to the amplifier.

For these reasons, you should locate the tank away from electro-magnetic fields and couple it loosely to the enclosure. Typical mounting techniques include placing the tank in a bag that is located on the bottom panel of the enclosure, or mounting the tank in a location that is acoustically isolated from the enclosure, for example by shock mounting. You should not mount the tank securely to the enclosure, especially in amplifiers with internal speakers.

## Grounding

Intuitively, you might think that the entire chassis acts as a ground, and that therefore components that are grounded can be connected to any point on the chassis. In fact, this is wrong, and haphazard grounding causes noise, especially hum and buzzing at multiples of the AC line frequency.

The steel and aluminum used to form chasses has some resistance, so if current is flowing through a chassis there will be a voltage drop across the chassis due to this internal resistance. If two points in the circuit are connected to grounds with different potentials, hum and buzzing can result, particularly when amplifying low-level signals in high-impedance stages with high gain.

To avoid this problem, you should ideally ground all components to one point on the chassis. The obvious choice for this central grounding point is where the ground lead of the AC cable is connected to the chassis. This technique is known as *star* grounding, because the ground connections radiate out from the central grounding point like rays of light from a star. This concept is illustrated in Figure 4.27.

**Figure 4.27** Star Grounding

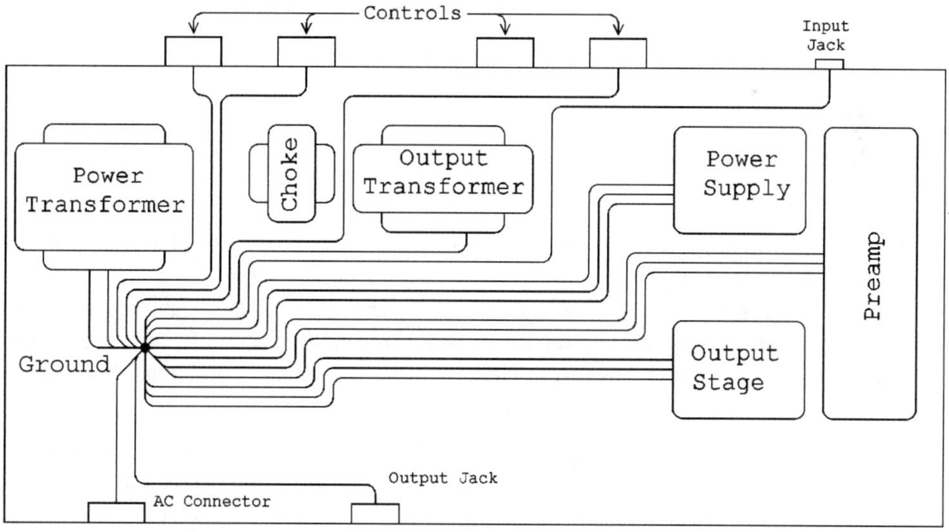


However, this approach can introduce stability and noise problems due to the long wire lengths needed to connect components located far from the star, and its proximity to the strong magnetic fields created by the power supply. It also requires a lot of ground wires, which can be messy and can affect reliability.

You can use a distributed star grounding approach to avoid these problems while still preventing ground loops. Each section of the circuit has its own local star ground, and then all of the local star grounds are connected to the master star ground as before. This concept is illustrated in Figure 4.28.

In Figure 4.28 the circuit is divided into four sections: the power transformer, the output stage, the power supply filters, and the preamplifier. Each section has its own star ground. The two center taps of the power transformer secondary windings are connected directly to the master star ground. The ground lead of the output transformer secondary winding and the grounds from the output stage are connected to the ground lug of the output jack, which is then connected to the master star ground. Note that the ground lug of the output jack contacts the chassis, so there is potential for a ground loop. However, the circuit impedances are low and the signal levels are high at this point, so a ground loop at this point will have little effect on the overall hum or noise. The grounds in the power supply filter section are tied to a local star ground, which is then connected to the master star ground.

**Figure 4.28** Distributed Star Grounding

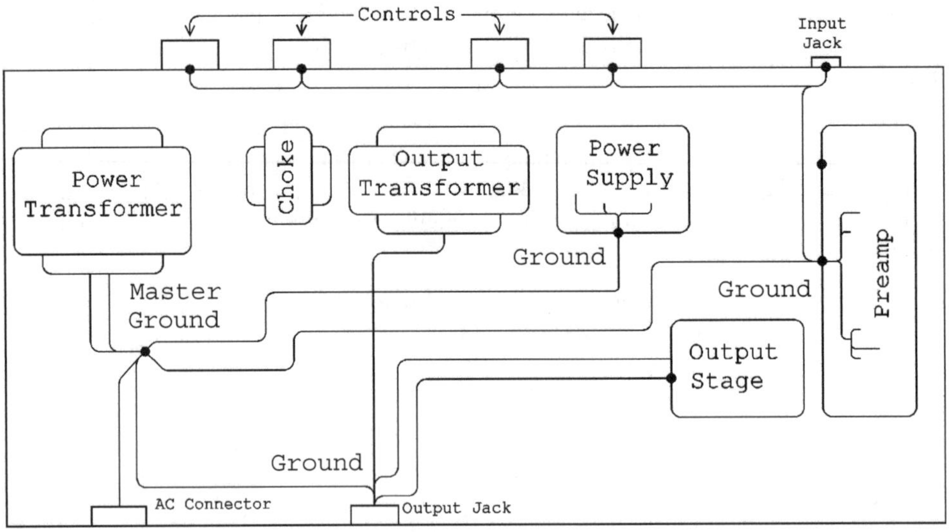


Finally, the preamplifier section grounds are connected to a local star ground, which is then connected to the master star ground. Note that ground connections from the controls and the input jack are also connected to the preamplifier local star ground, as these are part of the preamplifier circuit. The input jack ground must be isolated from the chassis, as this is the most sensitive part of the circuit and thus is most susceptible to ground loop problems. You isolate the input jack using the insulating washers shown in Figure 4.25.

Another advantage of distributed star grounding is that you can locate the last power supply filter sections close to the circuitry they feed. This can reduce noise and improve stability. When the final power supply filters are located in the preamplifier section, they are grounded to the preamplifier local star ground.

## Wiring

You should follow these guidelines when wiring your amplifier:

— Use distributed star grounding, as discussed above.

— Keep wires as short as possible by placing connected components close together, as discussed in the layout section.

— Twist wires that carry AC power together when possible. Twisting the wires helps to cancel the electromagnetic fields that radiate from the wires into adjacent circuitry, causing hum. This includes the leads for the power transformer primary, the high voltage and filament supply leads from the power transformer secondary, the leads from the choke, and the filament supply leads going to the tube sockets. Use solid-core wire for the filament supply connections, because solid-core wire is easier to twist and shape than stranded-core wire.

— Keep signal-carrying wires as far as possible from sources of hum, such as the power transformer, choke, and filter capacitors. Tuck the wiring for the controls near the front panel to take advantage of the shielding provided by the chassis.

— If you must locate components that carry sensitive signals far apart, or route signals close to hum-inducing components, use shielded cable with one end of the shield connected to ground. Common applications for shielded cable include connecting the input jack to the grid of the input stage amplifier, and routing signals to and from a master volume control located near the power supply.

A typical wiring scheme is shown in Figure 4.26. Note the routing of the wires to the controls and the use of a terminal strip to locate critical components close together near the output tubes. No shielded cable is used, because the input jack is located close to the input amplifier tube socket, and the master volume controls are located far enough from the power supply to avoid induced hum.

## Tools

### *Hand Tools*

Once you have designed your circuit and the chassis layout and procured the components, you can begin construction. The first step is to prepare the chassis for mounting the various components. You must drill or punch holes of various sizes and, in some cases, cut the chassis in other shapes. Metalworking tools required include:

1. A reversible, variable-speed drill with at least a 3/8” chuck.
2. Drill bits of various sizes, including a standard 1/16” through ¼” set, and 5/16”, 3/8”, and ½” bits to drill holes for the jacks and controls.
3. 7/8” and 1 1/8” chassis punches to make holes for the tube sockets.
4. Flat and round files.
5. A variable-speed jigsaw with metal-cutting blades.
6. A reamer is useful in some instances when holes need to be enlarged.

Mark the locations and sizes of the holes and other cutouts you need, and drill and cut them using the drill and jigsaw. Smooth any rough edges using files or the reamer. Finish all the metalwork before you mount the components – it's much easier to work on the naked chassis.

Once the chassis has been prepared, mount the components. Tools required include Philips and regular screwdrivers and wrenches of various sizes.

You need other hand tools to wire the circuit, including a *wire stripper* to remove insulation from hookup wire, and *long-nosed pliers* to guide and crimp wires and component leads.

## Soldering

Proper soldering is essential to successful amplifier construction. If you don't know how to solder, you must learn before you begin construction. Many problems encountered when troubleshooting prototype amplifiers are due to poor solder joints.

Tools used in soldering include a *soldering iron* and *solder*. A typical 40W soldering iron used in amplifier construction is shown in Figure 4.29. Note the adjustment to vary the temperature and the wet sponge, which is used to clean the tip of the iron. You can buy tips of various shapes and sizes.

**Figure 4.29** Typical Soldering Station

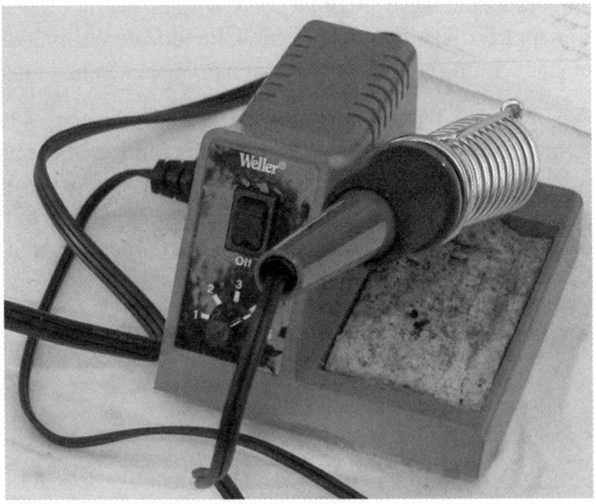


In some situations, for example, when soldering directly to the chassis, a larger, more powerful iron is needed. Sources for soldering irons can be found in Appendix A.

The solder used should be rosin core, and have a diameter of around .05". In the past, solder has generally been made from lead and tin, but modern lead-free solders are now available, albeit at a higher price.

To solder a joint, you:

1. Connect all the wires and other components to the soldering joint. The joint should be securely fastened to the chassis, for example, a lug on a terminal strip or potentiometer or a tube socket pin. Each wire or component lead should go through the lug or pin and then be crimped tightly to provide some mechanical support.

2. Heat the joint with the tip of the soldering iron. All the wires, component leads, and the lug or pin itself must be heated.
3. Apply solder to the joint. You will see the solder begin to melt and pool on the joint. Eventually, the solder will flow freely throughout the joint and cover all of the wires, component leads, and the lug or pin. Apply enough solder to fill the joint, but not so much that excess solder drips off the joint onto other parts of the circuit.
4. Remove the solder and the iron, and wait for the joint to cool and the solder to solidify. Do not move any wires or leads while the joint is cooling.

If you are not skilled in soldering, you should practice using some old components and equipment until you develop the ability to solder properly.

You also need to be able to unsolder connections, for example, when replacing faulty components. The easiest way to unsolder a joint is to first heat the joint until the solder liquefies, and then remove the solder from the joint using a *solder sucker.* Solder suckers can either be a rubber bulb that you squeeze or a spring-operated pump. In both cases, you place the tip of the sucker close to the joint and suck out the liquefied solder. You can then unwrap the leads and disassemble the joint. You may have to repeat the heating/sucking process a few times before the lead can be removed from the joint. Excessive flexing of the lead or joint can result in breakage due to metal fatigue, so be careful.

# Testing and Troubleshooting

## *Test Equipment*

You need the following basic test equipment to test and troubleshoot amplifiers:

A *digital volt meter (DVM)* measures AC and DC voltages, resistance, and, in some units, capacitance. Make sure that the DVM you choose can measure DC voltages up to at least 500V. A typical DVM is shown in Figure 4.30.

**Figure 4.30** Typical DVM

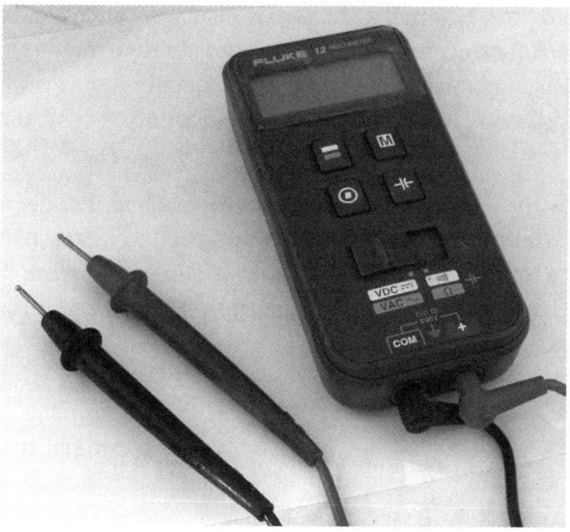

An *audio signal generator* produces sine waves in the audio frequency range, usually 20Hz to 20kHz or more. Frequency and output level are adjustable. A typical audio signal generator is shown in Figure 4.31.

**Figure 4.31** Typical Audio Signal Generator

An *oscilloscope* displays signal waveforms. A *probe* is used to connect to the point in the circuit that you want to monitor. Normally, the y-axis displays voltage and the x-axis displays time. Oscilloscopes have controls to adjust the voltage per division on the y-axis and the time per division on the x-axis, and most can display two channels at the same time. A simple, basic unit is all that is needed for amplifier test and troubleshooting. A typical oscilloscope is shown in Figure 4.32.

A *variac* is used to vary the AC supply voltage provided to a unit under test. As we will see in the next section, when you power up an amplifier you need to increase the supply voltage slowly to avoid damage to the unit. A typical variac is shown in Figure 4.33. Note the large adjustment knob, which varies the output voltage from 0 to 140VAC.

**Figure 4.32** Typical Oscilloscope for Audio Applications

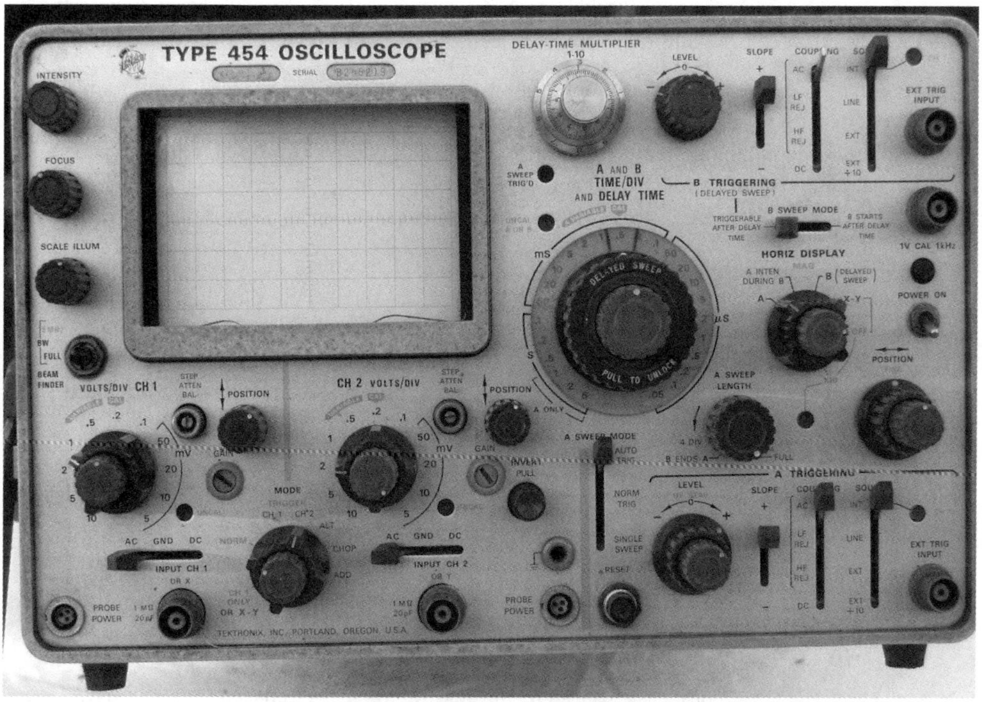


**Figure 4.33** Typical Variac

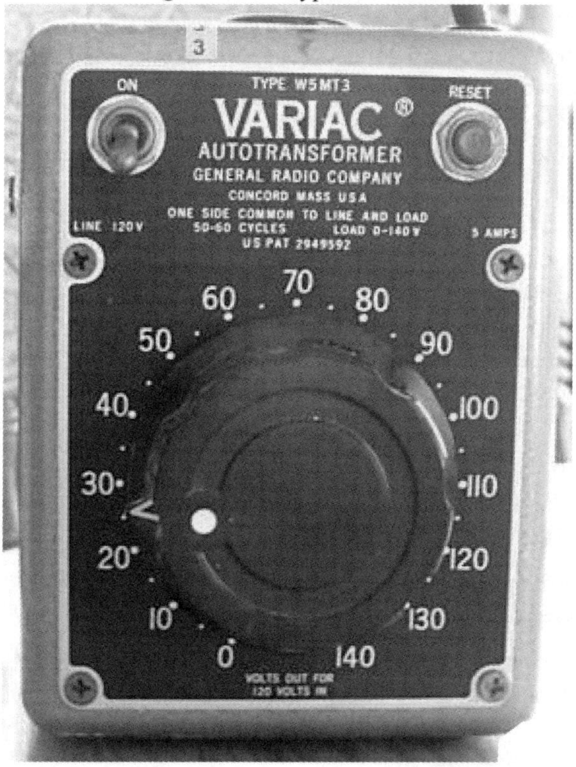

A *dummy load* is a high-power resistor that you connect to the output to simulate a speaker. The resistance should equal the output impedance of the amplifier, for example, 8Ω, and the wattage should exceed the output power of the amplifier under test.

There are many other types of equipment that are useful in design and testing; the items listed above represent a minimal set that will allow you to test and troubleshoot amplifiers effectively. DVMs, signal generators, oscilloscopes, and variacs can be obtained from the sources listed in Appendix A. They can also be purchased used, at very reasonable prices, on the Internet. You can use PC-based software to implement a signal generator or oscilloscope.

After you finish assembling your amplifier, you should first check all of the components and connections against the schematic. Check each section of the circuit, paying particular attention to the solder joints. If a joint seems suspect, grab and wiggle each lead with long-nosed pliers to check for looseness. Check carefully for any short-circuits between ground and the DC supplies or the AC supply wiring. Also, make sure that all electrolytic capacitors are properly polarized.

## *Initial Power-up*

Once you are confident that the circuit is wired correctly, the initial power-up procedure is as follows:

1. Make sure the power and standby switches are off. Install a 1A fast-blow fuse. Do not install any tubes.
2. Make sure the variac power is off and its output voltage is set to 0V. Plug in the variac, and plug the amplifier power cord into the variac output receptacle.
3. Connect the negative lead of the DVM to the chassis and the positive lead to the positive terminal of the first power supply filter capacitor. Make sure that neither of the test leads is shorted to any other part of the amplifier. You can use short, insulated test leads with alligator clips on each end to make the connections.
4. Turn on the variac and amplifier power switches. Slowly turn up the variac output voltage to around 10VAC. Check the DC voltage at the positive terminal of the first power supply capacitor – it should be around 40VDC. Gradually raise the variac output voltage to full voltage. The DC voltage on the capacitor should also rise, and should be slightly higher than the nominal supply voltage at full AC input voltage. You should charge electrolytic capacitors that are new or that haven't been charged up recently gradually in this manner to prevent possible catastrophic failure. In addition, if the amplifier is wired incorrectly there may be short circuits that result in excessive current flow through certain components. Increasing the supply voltage gradually allows you to localize any overheated components before they are destroyed or the fuse blows.
5. Using the DVM, measure the filament voltage at each tube socket. It should be $6.3VAC_{rms}$ for the preamplifier and output tubes, and $5VAC_{rms}$ for the rectifier tube, if used.
6. Turn off the amplifier power switch and monitor the DC voltage on the capacitor. It should gradually decrease to 0VDC as the capacitor discharges through the discharge resistor.
7. Reduce the variac output voltage to 0VAC, and turn the power and standby switches on. Again, gradually raise the variac output voltage while monitoring the DC voltage on the capacitor. The DC voltage should again rise to slightly higher than the nominal supply voltage.

8. Carefully remove the positive lead of the DVM from the capacitor, making sure not to touch the uninsulated part of the lead or to short the lead to any part of the circuit or chassis. Holding the insulated handle of the positive lead, measure the DC voltages at the following points in the circuit:

   a. the positive terminals of each of the power supply filter capacitors,

   b. the plate pins on the output tube sockets (normally pin 3),

   c. the screen grid pins on the output tube sockets (normally pin 4), and

   d. the plate pins in the preamplifier tube sockets (pins 1 and 6 for 12A_7 tubes).

   All of these voltages should be the same as the voltage measured at the first filter capacitor.

9. If your amplifier uses grid biasing, measure the DC voltage at the negative terminal of the bias supply filter capacitor, and note the voltage. Measure the voltage at the wiper of the bias adjustment potentiometer, and vary the control while monitoring the DC voltage; it should vary over a range of negative DC voltages on the order of -10VDC to -60VDC, depending on the design.

10. Turn the power and standby switches off and wait a minute or two for the power supply capacitors to discharge. Check the voltage on the power supply capacitors to make sure they have fully discharged. Replace the fuse with the proper value slow-blow fuse. Plug in the preamplifier tubes, but not the output tubes. Turn the power switch on and check to make sure that the filaments in the tubes glow.

11. Turn on the standby switch and measure the DC voltages at these points in the circuit:

    a. the positive terminal of the first power supply capacitor, which should still be slightly higher than the nominal supply voltage,

    b. the positive terminal of the second power supply capacitor, which should be at or a few volts below the voltage at the first capacitor,

    c. the positive terminal of the third power supply filter capacitor, which should be 25-50V lower than the nominal supply voltage, because the preamplifier tubes are now drawing current, causing a voltage drop across the resistor between the second and third power supply capacitors,

    d. the positive terminal of the fourth (and, if there is one, fifth) power supply filter capacitor, which should again be 25-50V lower than the preceding capacitor,

    e. the plates of each preamplifier tube section (pins 1 and 6 for 12A_7 tubes), which should be 100-150V lower than the supply voltage to their load resistors,

    f. the cathodes of each preamplifier tube section (pins 3 and 8 for 12A_7 tubes), which should be around 1-3V,

    g. the plates of the phase splitter (for PP amplifiers), which should be around the same voltage as the preamplifier tube plates, and

    h. the cathodes of the phase splitter, which should be around 40-60V.

    If all of these voltages are as indicated, the power supply is probably operating correctly, and the preamplifier and phase splitter tubes are conducting current and self-biasing properly.

12. Turn off the standby switch and wait a minute or two for the power supply capacitors to discharge. Check the voltage on the power supply capacitors to make sure they have fully discharged. Adjust the bias control so that the bias voltage is as negative as possible. Connect the dummy load to the speaker output. Plug in the output tubes and confirm that the output tube filaments are glowing. Turn on the standby switch.

13. For grid-biased output stages, assuming that you have placed current-sensing resistors between the cathodes of the output tubes and ground, measure the DC voltage at the cathode of each output tube. If the resistors are 10Ω, each mA of current will cause a voltage drop of 0.01V across the resistor. So, for example, if you want a quiescent bias current of 35mA, the voltage across the resistor should be 0.35V. Gradually increase the bias voltage while monitoring the voltage across the current-sensing resistor. As the bias voltage becomes more positive, the current should increase until it reaches the desired value. Check both tubes, and, if the voltages are different, adjust the bias voltage so that the current through both tubes is as close as possible to the desired value.

14. For cathode-biased output stages, measure the voltage across the cathode resistor. Using Ohm's law and the value of the resistor, calculate the current flowing through the resistor and confirm that it is close to the desired quiescent bias current.

    If these voltages are as indicated, the power supply is operating correctly, and the output tubes are biased properly and conducting current.

## *Testing With AC Signals*

Once you have adjusted the bias and confirmed that the quiescent DC voltages are correct, you can connect your amplifier to a speaker and test it further by playing through it. However, you can learn more using a signal generator and an oscilloscope to check its operation under signal conditions.

The basic test setup is shown in Figure 4.34. The signal generator is connected to the amplifier input, and the dummy load is connected to the speaker output. The oscilloscope and DVM are used to monitor and measure signals at various points in the circuit.

**Figure 4.34** Basic Test Setup

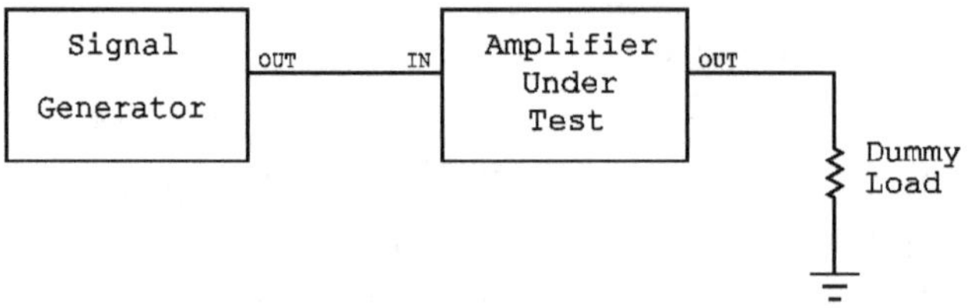


You can test the circuit in many ways. The following procedure will confirm that all stages are functioning properly; it is assumed you are testing a design similar to the one described in Chapter 2, where the tone and volume controls are located between the input and second stage amplifiers:

1. Set the signal generator to output a sine wave at 400Hz with an output level around 1V.
2. Set the oscilloscope time/div to 1msec and volts/div to 0.5V. Set the trigger to normal.

3. Connect the signal generator output directly to the oscilloscope input and confirm that the signal generator waveform is displayed on the oscilloscope. If you do not see the signal, adjust the oscilloscope controls as needed.

4. Reduce the signal generator output level to 100mV, and connect it to the amplifier input. Connect the 10x probe to the oscilloscope input, and clip the probe's ground connector to the amplifier chassis.

5. Set the amplifier controls as follows: treble, middle, bass, and presence at 5, and all volume controls at 0.

6. Turn on the amplifier's power and standby switches. Connect the probe to the plate of the input amplifier. You should see a sine wave on the oscilloscope. If not, adjust the volts/div setting and the trigger as needed. Remember, even though the volts/div setting is 0.5V/div, the actual vertical scale is 5V/div because the probe attenuates the signal by 10 times. Note the signal voltage – it should be the input voltage level times the gain of the stage.

7. Move the probe to the plate of the second stage amplifier. Gradually increase the volume control until you see a sine wave on the oscilloscope. Reduce the signal generator frequency to 100Hz, and adjust the bass control up and down. Confirm that the signal level changes with the position of the control. Increase the signal generator frequency to 1kHz. Adjust the middle control and confirm that the signal level changes with the position of the control. Increase the signal generator frequency to 5kHz. Adjust the treble control up and down and confirm that the signal level changes with the position of the control. During these tests you will have to adjust the time/div on the oscilloscope to see the waveform clearly.

8. If the amplifier has a PP output stage, move the probe to one plate of the phase splitter. If the amplifier has a master volume control, turn it up until you see signal on the oscilloscope. If there is no master volume control, adjust the volts/div on the oscilloscope for a clear signal trace. Move the probe to the other plate of the phase splitter and confirm that the signal levels on the two plates are similar. If you have a two-channel oscilloscope and two probes, connect one to each plate, display both signals, and confirm that they are out of phase.

9. Move the probe to the dummy load, and adjust the oscilloscope for a clear signal trace. Reconfirm the proper operation of all controls previously tested. If the amplifier has a presence control, confirm that it changes the signal level at a frequency of 5kHz.

10. To check the maximum output power, increase the volume while monitoring the signal across the dummy load on the oscilloscope. Note the peak-to-peak voltage at which the output signal begins to clip. Divide this voltage by 2.8 to get the rms voltage, and calculate the power output using the formula $W = \frac{V^2}{R}$, where R is the resistance of the dummy load. The load resistor may get hot, so be careful.

11. If the amplifier has other features such as effects, you can perform additional tests similar to those above to confirm that the added circuitry is performing as expected.

## *Troubleshooting*

All of the test procedures discussed previously assume that the amplifier is functioning as intended. Of course, this is not always the case, so this section will discuss how to troubleshoot and fix common problems found in newly-constructed amplifiers. Repairing older amplifiers is somewhat different, because the failures are mostly due to aging components, which is normally not an issue with new construction.

Most new amplifiers that do not perform properly do so for one of the following reasons:

— Incorrect design.

— Wiring mistakes, including wrong component values and errors in connecting components.

— Bad solder joints.

— Poor layout.

— Faulty components.

In some instances you may think the amplifier is not performing properly when in reality the test conditions cause the problem. For example, excessive distortion can be caused by an input signal that is at too high a level or, if you connect the oscilloscope probe to the dummy load so that the ground connection is attached to the ungrounded output, you will short the output and see no signal. So, before you conclude something is wrong with the amplifier, make sure you check the test setup first.

The basic methodology of troubleshooting is to first isolate the problem to a specific stage of the amplifier, then determine what in that stage is causing the problem. For example, if you see a problem at the speaker output, next check the output stage driver to see if the problem is there as well. Continue back through the stages until you find a stage where the problem no longer exists; then, the problem must be in the following stage. Stages with feedback can be difficult to troubleshoot in this way, as the feedback will affect all of the stages in the feedback loop. Sometimes, including in the output stages discussed in this book, you can disconnect the feedback loop to help troubleshoot the stages. In other cases you have to use different techniques.

If the amplifier blows the fuse when you first check the DC conditions, as discussed in the previous section, you know that the problem is either in the power transformer primary circuit, the filament supply circuit, or the high voltage secondary/rectifier/first filter capacitor section. You can isolate the problem in some instances by turning up the variac to a low voltage that will not blow the fuse, and then looking for overheating components. Sometimes the component will begin to smoke, and sometimes you can feel or smell the heat. If this approach doesn't isolate the problem, follow the troubleshooting procedure described below. If the initial power-up is successful but the fuse blows when you turn on the standby switch, apply the same technique to the rest of the power supply circuit.

Once you have isolated the problem to a specific stage, you can use several approaches to determine exactly what is wrong:

1. If the problem is in an amplifier stage, swap the tube with a known good replacement.
2. Check all of the components and connections in the stage.
3. Measure the DC voltages at all points in the circuit to confirm that they are reasonable. If you find a point where the DC voltage is unreasonable, check the components wired to that point.
4. With the unit powered up and the amplifier connected to a speaker, tap on all of the components and connections with a wooden stick and listen for changes in the output. If tapping a certain connection causes the signal to change, turn off the power and resolder the joint, then recheck the connection. If tapping a component creates the change and resoldering does not solve the problem, replace the component with a known good component.
5. If the stage is oscillating, check the grounding and the wire routing. In some cases, you may have to add low-value bypass capacitors, between 47pf and 1nf, to the grid or plate of the stage to stop the oscillation.
6. If you still haven't identified the problem, you can disassemble the stage and replace the components with known good components.

## Common Problems

Common problems associated with new amplifier construction include:

1. Output stage oscillation – If the preamplifier stages function correctly, but you see oscillation at the speaker output of a PP amplifier when the output tubes are installed, you may have reversed the output transformer primary leads going to the tube sockets. This results in positive feedback, causing oscillation. You can fix this by switching either the primary leads (not the center tap) or the connections to the grids of the output tubes.
2. Potentiometer wiring – You must determine how to wire the controls so that, for example, when you turn the volume control clockwise the volume increases. For volume controls, looking at the back of the potentiometer with the solder lugs up, the left-hand lug should be grounded. Other controls, such as the treble control, do not have any of the terminals grounded, so you may have to try different wiring schemes to determine the proper configuration.
3. If you mistakenly reverse the polarity of an electrolytic capacitor, leakage current will flow at a voltage much lower than the rated voltage. If the capacitor is in the power supply, it will heat rapidly and then explode unless you turn off the power quickly. If the capacitor is bypassing a cathode resistor, the DC operating conditions may be upset, or you may notice excessive distortion.

4. Short circuits – When you solder a wire, the heat applied can melt the insulation near the joint. If the wire passes close to another connection point, for example, on a tube socket, it can short. You can also melt the insulation on an adjacent wire when soldering a connection. You should wire the filament circuit first, and keep the filament wiring close to the chassis to help avoid shorts around the tube sockets.

5. Open circuits – You can forget to solder a joint, or a component or wire can pop out of the joint while the solder is cooling, or an adjacent joint can be loosened while soldering a connection, causing an open circuit.

6. Missing components or wiring - You can forget to include components or connecting wires.

7. Loose connections – As discussed earlier in this chapter, loose connections caused by poor soldering cause many problems, and these problems are among the most difficult to troubleshoot.

8. Poor grounding – If the amplifier passes signals but is noisy, your grounding scheme may be to blame. In some cases, components intended to be isolated from the chassis, such as the input jack, may be shorted to the chassis due to improper mounting. In other cases, components may be shorted to hardware such as standoffs.

# Appendix A
# Sources for Components

**Electronic Component Suppliers:** resistors, capacitors, potentiometers, switches, fuses, hardware, prototyping board, tools and test equipment.

— Digi-Key: www.digikey.com

— Mouser Electronics: www.mouser.com

**Specialized Components for Tube Amplifiers:** tubes, sockets, transformers, chokes, and special components for tube circuits.

— Antique Electronics: www.tubesandmore.com

— Magic Parts: www.magicparts.com

— Hammond Manufacturing: www.hammondmfg.com – a major supplier of transformers and chasses

— Old Colony Sound Lab: www.audioxpress.com – a good source for books and some test equipment

— Parts Express: www.parts-express.com – a good source for some components, tools, and test equipment

— Weber Speakers: www.tedweber.com

— The Web: you can find lots of specialized components on E-Bay and other on-line auction sites, and through various forums and Web sites dedicated to tube amplifiers (see the Bibliography for some examples)

All of the companies listed above offer on-line and traditional catalogs.

# Appendix B
# Tube Data

This appendix lists data for the most common preamplifier, output, and rectifier tubes used in guitar amplifiers. You can use this information to determine appropriate transformer and power supply parameters for your design, and you can copy and use the characteristic curves to design the various stages. Remember, you will need two copies of the output tube characteristic curves to design a PP output stage, as explained in Chapter 2. Furthermore, the data shown is only valid for the listed screen grid voltage.

Figure B.1 shows the pin connections for the entire 12A_7 family of preamplifier tubes. You will also note that the octal output tubes have similar pin connections. However, pay close attention to the suppressor grid connection on the 6CA7 tube, which must be tied externally to the cathode.

More detailed data on these tubes, as well as data on other tubes of interest, can be found in tube data books and on the Internet. Useful references are listed in the bibliography.

## Preamplifier Tubes

**Figure B.1** 12A_7A Pinout

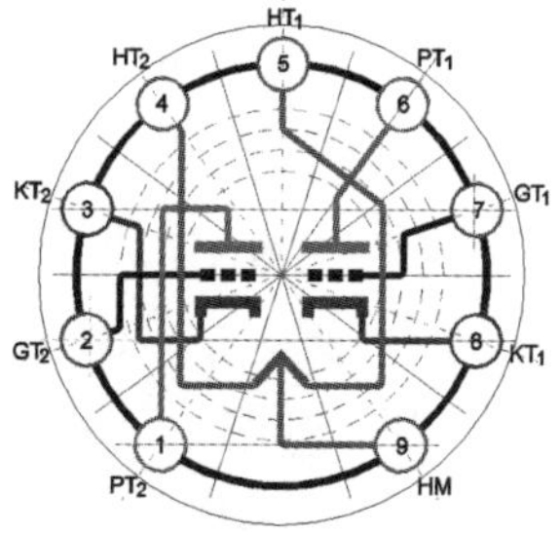

## *12AX7A/ECC83/7025*

Note: 7025 is low-noise version.

Heater current: 0.3 A @ 6.3 V (parallel connection)
Heater-cathode voltage: +/-200 V peak, 100 V avg.
Max. plate voltage: 330 V
Max. plate dissipation: 1.2 W

**Figure B.2** 12AX7A Characteristic Curves

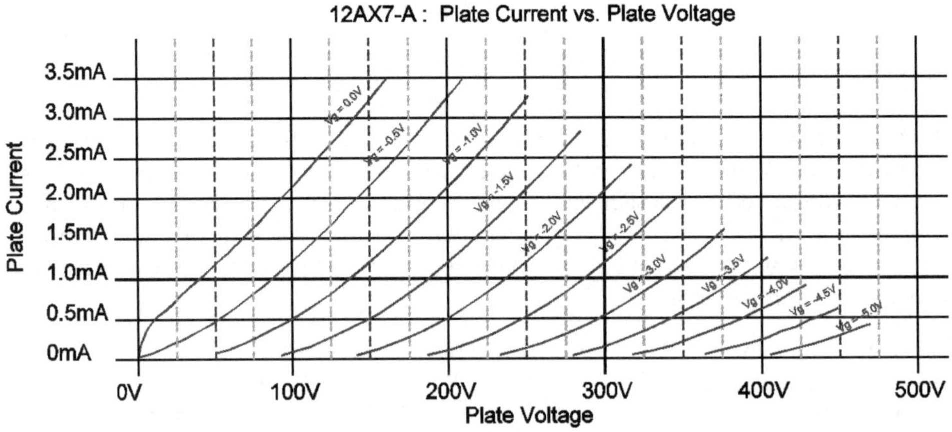

## *12AU7A/ECC82*

Heater current: 0.3 A @ 6.3 V (parallel connection)
Heater-cathode voltage: +/-200 V peak, 100 V avg.
Max. plate voltage: 330 V
Max. cathode current: 22 mA
Max. plate dissipation: 2.75 W (each plate), 5.5 W (both plates)

**Figure B.3** 12AU7A Characteristic Curves

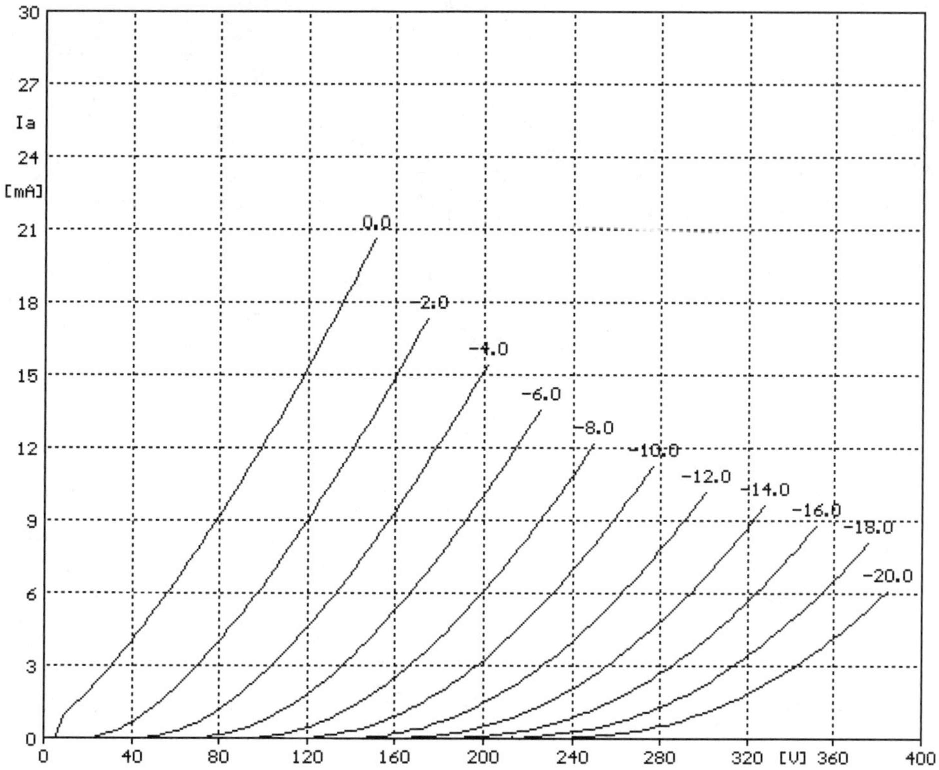

## *12AT7/ECC81*

Heater current: 0.3 A @ 6.3 V (parallel connection)
Heater-cathode voltage: +/-100 V peak
Max. plate voltage: 330 V
Max. plate dissipation: 2.8 W

**Figure B.4** 12AT7 Characteristic Curves

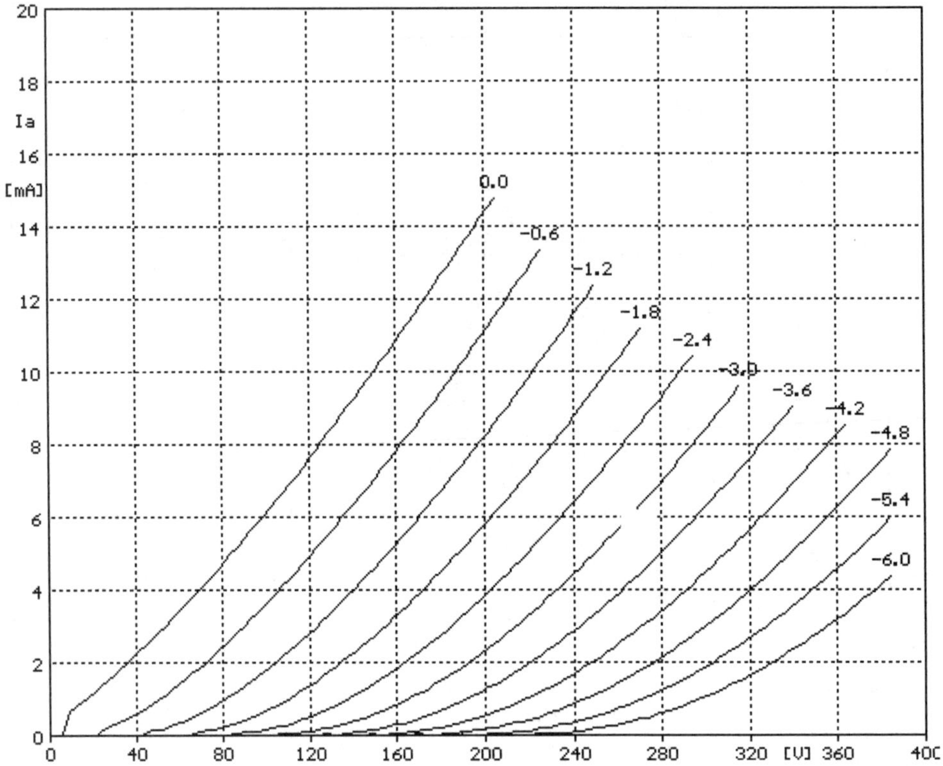

# Power Tubes

The characteristic curves for the pentode output tubes in this section are shown for a single screen grid voltage. If you change the screen grid voltage, the characteristic curves will also change. If you lower the screen grid voltage the curves shift lower on the y-axis; that is, for a given control grid voltage the plate current is lower. If you raise the screen grid voltage the opposite occurs.

If you need to know the characteristic curves for a different screen grid voltage, you can look for published characteristic curves at the desired screen voltage, or you can calculate the new curves. To calculate the new curves, you need data showing plate current versus control grid voltage at various screen grid voltages, which you can usually find in the tube data sheet. This data is taken at a specified plate voltage. If data for the desired screen grid voltage is shown, you transfer data points from the curve to the characteristic curves and draw new curves which follow the shape of the existing curves. If data for the desired screen voltage is not shown, you interpolate between the curves shown and proceed as before.

For example, let's say you want to determine the characteristic curves for the 6BQ5, shown in Figure B.6, at a screen grid voltage of 200 V, rather than at 250 V as shown. You obtain the curves for the 6BQ5 that show plate current versus control grid voltage for a plate voltage of 250 V at various screen grid voltages, and see that, at a control grid voltage of 0 V and a screen grid voltage of 200 V, the plate current is 130 mA. You plot this point on the existing characteristic curves (plate voltage = 250 V, plate current = 130 mA), and draw a curve that follows, but in this case is lower than, the existing curve for a control grid voltage of 0 V and a screen grid voltage of 250 V. Repeat this process for other control grid voltages, until you have a complete new set of curves.

More information on deriving characteristic curves at different screen grid voltages can be found in several of the references, including Blencowe's *Designing Valve Preamplifiers for Guitar and Bass* and Langford-Smith's *Radiotron Designer's Handbook.*

Note: Maximum ratings shown are for the first type listed in a group. Other listed types may have different maximum ratings.

## *6BQ5/EL84*

Heater current: 0.76 A @ 6.3 V
Max. plate voltage: 300 V
Max. screen grid voltage: 300 V
Max. plate dissipation: 12 W
Max. screen grid dissipation: 2 W
Max. control grid resistance: 0.3 MΩ (fixed bias), 1 MΩ (cathode bias)

**Figure B.5** 6BQ5 Pinout

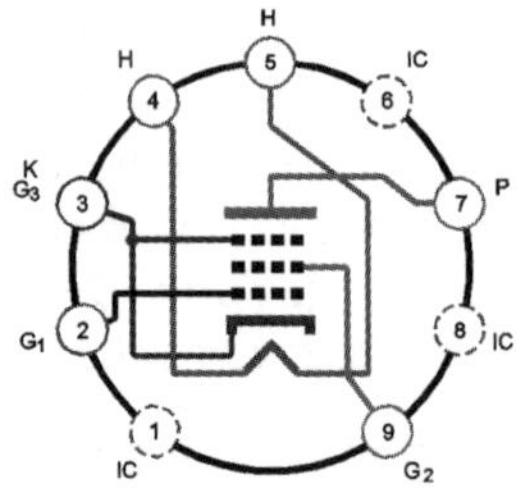


**Figure B.6** 6BQ5 Characteristic Curves

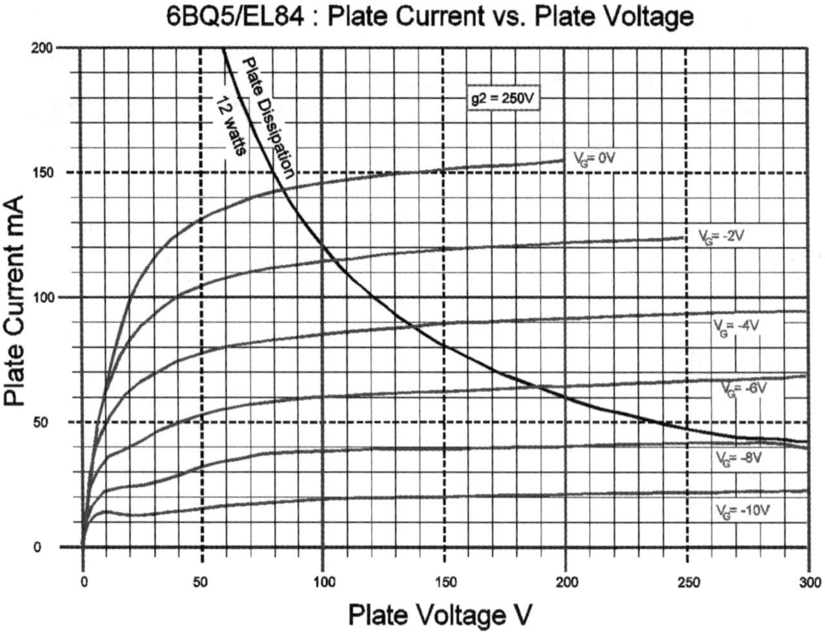

## *6V6GTA/6AQ5A*

Heater current: 0.45 A @ 6.3 V
Max. plate voltage: 350 V
Max. screen grid voltage: 315 V
Max. plate dissipation: 14 W
Max. screen grid dissipation: 2.2 W
Max. control grid resistance: 0.1 MΩ (fixed bias), 0.5 MΩ (cathode bias)

**Figure B.7** 6V6GTA Pinout

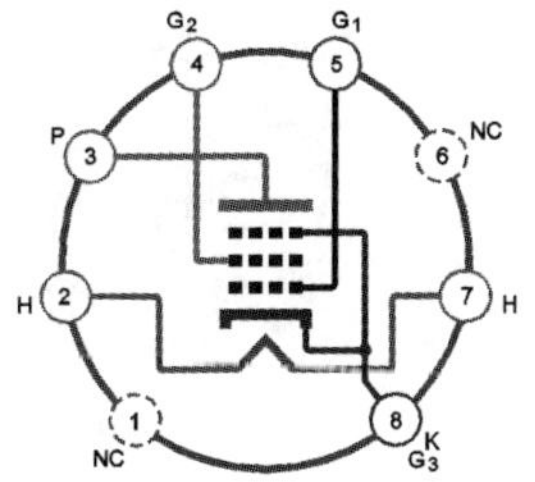


**Figure B.8** 6V6GTA Characteristic Curves

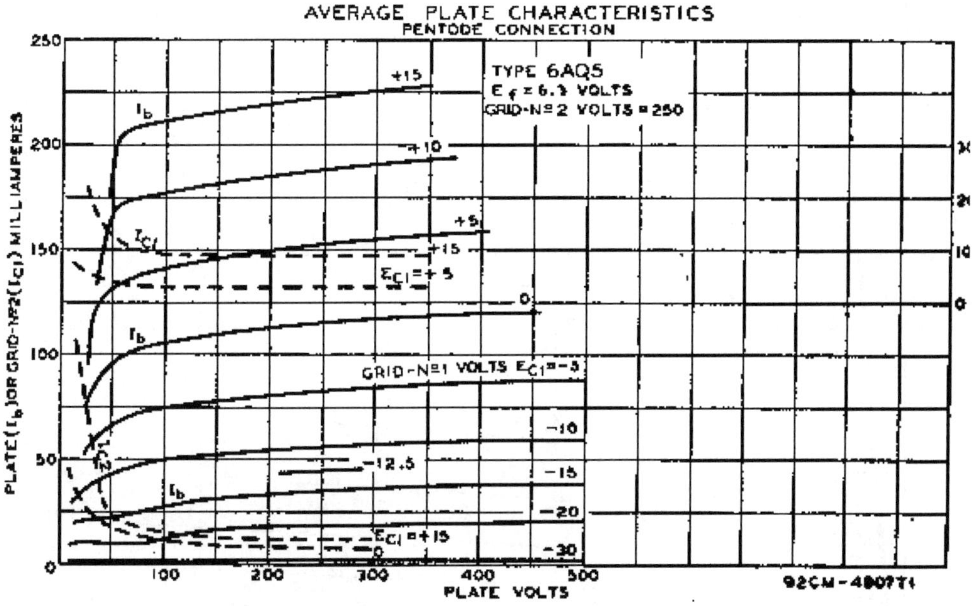

## *6L6GC/7027A/5881/KT66*

Heater current: 0.9 A @ 6.3 V
Max. plate voltage: 500 V
Max. screen grid voltage: 450 V
Max. plate dissipation: 30 W
Max. screen grid dissipation: 5 W
Max. control grid resistance: 0.1 MΩ (fixed bias), 0.5 MΩ (cathode bias)

**Figure B.9** 6L6GC Pinout]

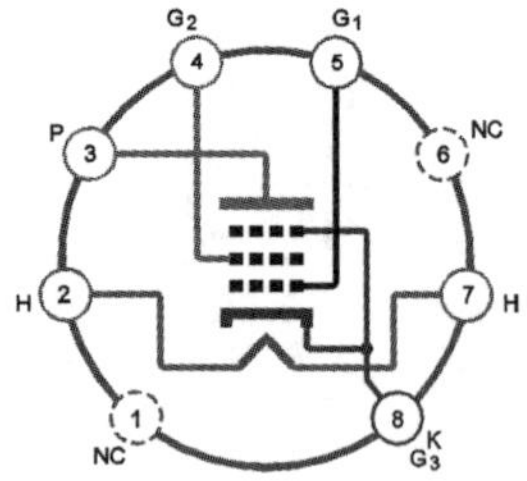


**Figure B.10** 6L6GC Characteristic Curves

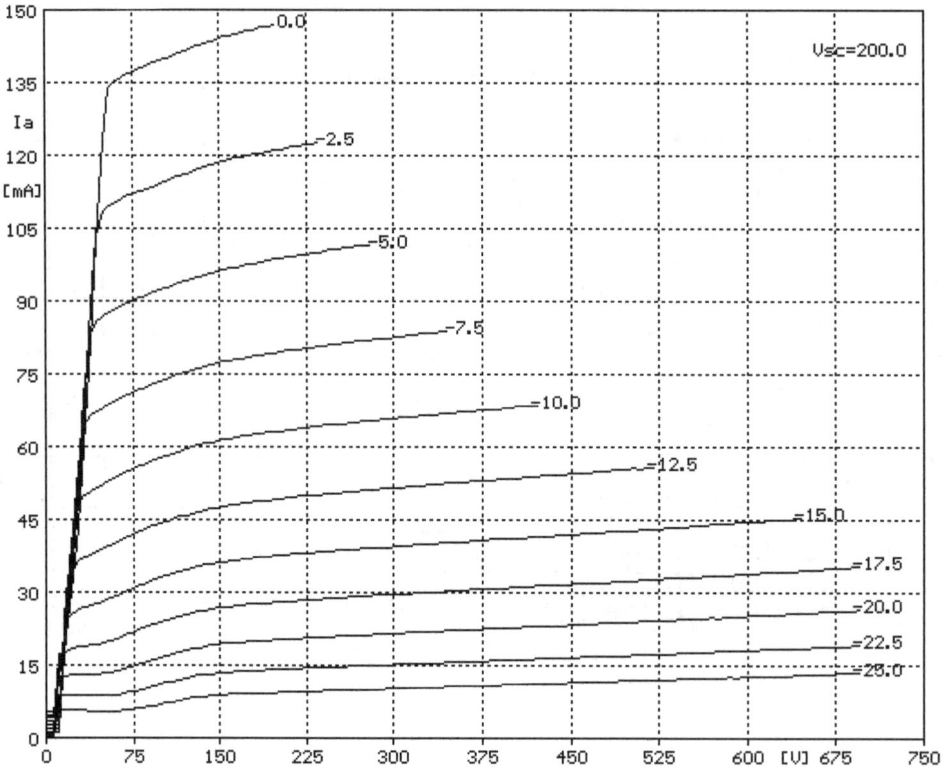

## *6CA7/EL34/KT77*

Heater current: 1.5 A @ 6.3 V
Max. plate voltage: 800 V
Max. screen grid voltage: 425 V
Max. plate dissipation: 25 W
Max. screen grid dissipation: 8 W
Max. control grid resistance: 0.7 MΩ (cathode bias)

**Figure B.11** 6CA7 Pinout

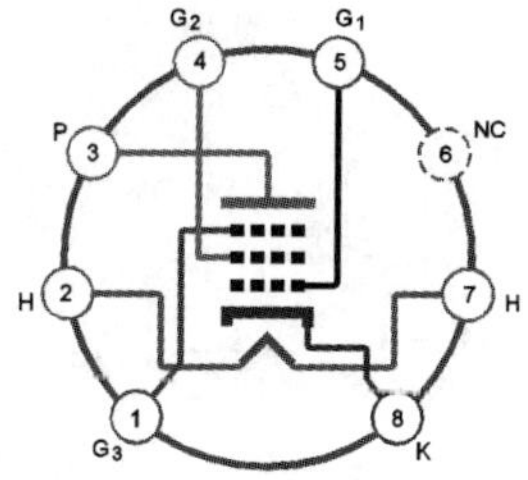


**Figure B.12** 6CA7 Characteristic Curves

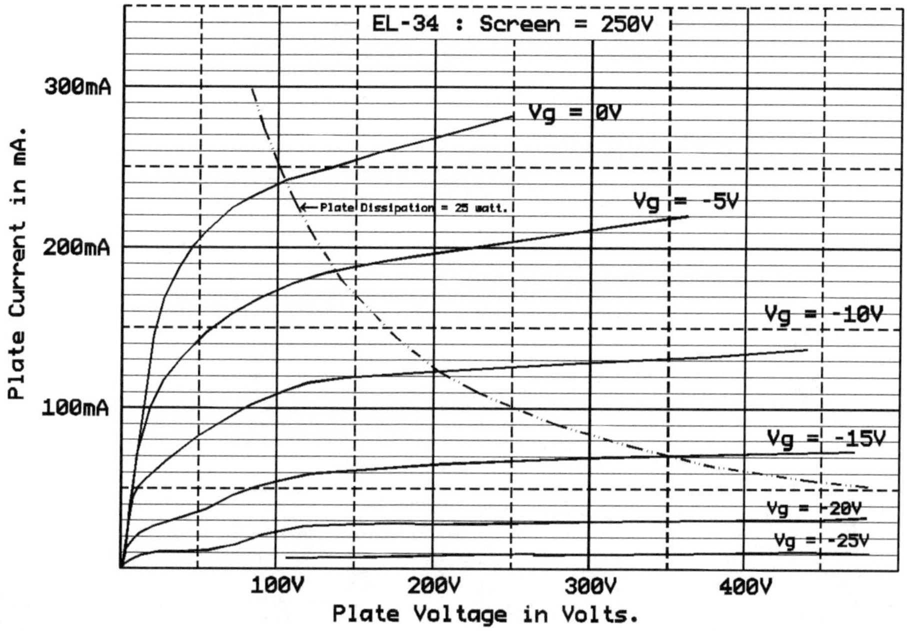

## *6550/KT88*

Heater current: 1.6 A @ 6.3 V
Max. plate voltage: 600 V
Max. screen grid voltage: 400 V
Max. plate dissipation: 35 W
Max. screen grid dissipation: 6 W
Max. control grid resistance: 0.05 MΩ (fixed bias), 0.25 MΩ (cathode bias)

**Figure B.13** 6550 Pinout

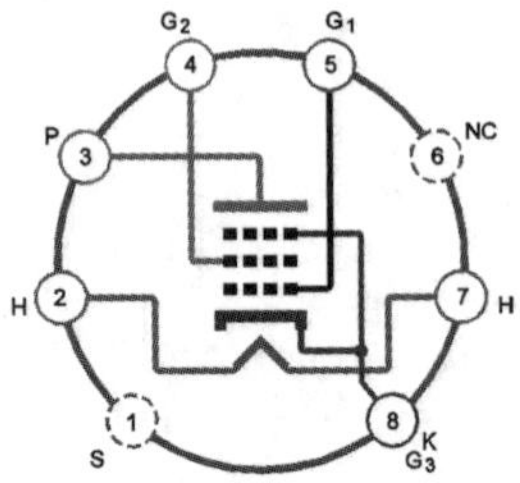


**Figure B.14** 6550 Characteristic Curves

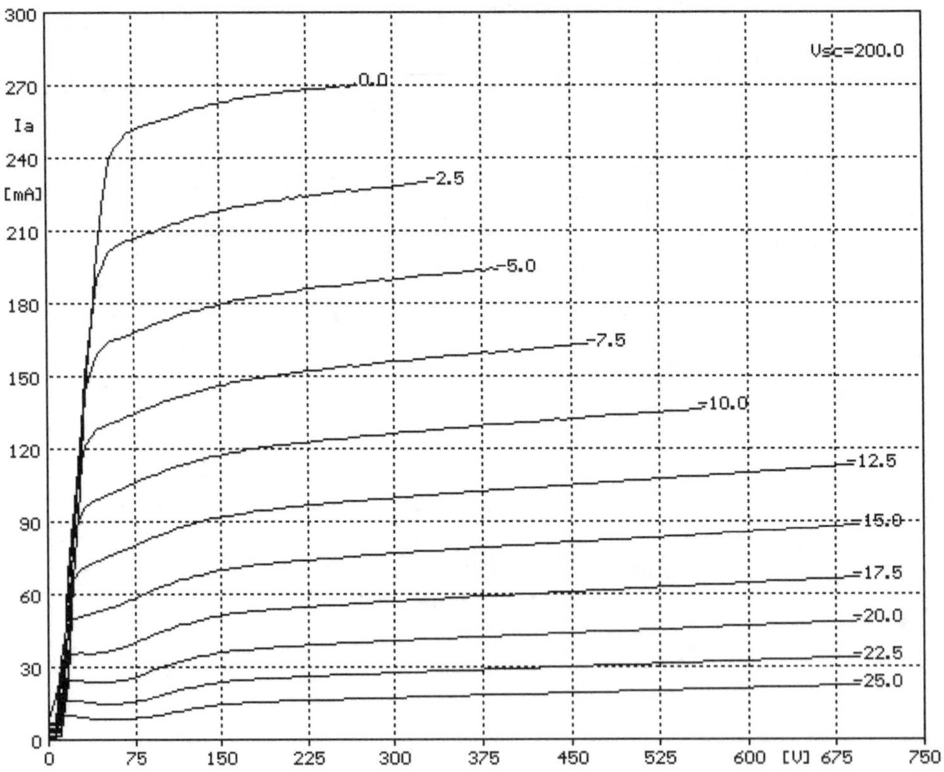

## Rectifier Tubes

### *5Y3GT*

Heater current: 2 A @ 5 V
Max. peak inverse plate voltage: 1400 V
Max. peak plate current (each plate): 440 mA
Max. input filter capacitor value, 700 Vrms plate-plate supply: 20 ufd
Effective plate impedance, 700 Vrms plate-plate supply: 50Ω per plate
DC output voltage, 700 Vrms plate-plate supply, 125 mA full-load current: 360 V
DC output voltage, 700 Vrms plate-plate supply, 62.5 mA half-load current: 390 V

**Figure B.15** 5Y3GT Pinout

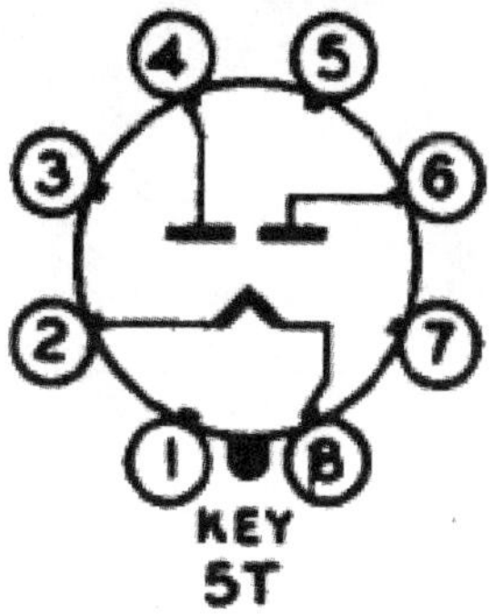


### *5AR4/GZ34*

Heater current: 1.9 A @ 5 V
Max. peak inverse plate voltage: 1700 V
Max. peak plate current (each plate): 825 mA
Max. input filter capacitor value: 60 ufd
Effective plate impedance, 450 Vrms plate-plate supply: 160Ω per plate
DC output voltage, 450 Vrms plate-plate supply, 225 mA average current: 475 V

**Figure B.16** 5AR4 Pinout

# Bibliography

*Basic Theory and Application of Electron Tubes* (Peterborough, NH: Audio Amateur, Inc.). A reprint of US Army Technical Manual TM 11-662, dated February 1952.

Blencowe, Merlin *Designing Tube Preamps for Guitar and Bass* (self-published, 2009).

Blencowe, Merlin *Designing Power Supplies for Tube Amplifiers* (self-published, 2010)

http://www.accutronicsreverb.com - Includes information on spring reverb tanks, associated circuitry, and reverberation in general.

http://www.aikenamps.com/ - Aiken Amps site. The "Tech Info Link" leads to several interesting papers, including a detailed analysis of phase-shift oscillator design.

http://www.audioxpress.com/resource/audioclass/index.htm - Includes a number of articles on tube amp design by Joe Marshall and Norman Crowhurst.

http://www.ax84.com – A site dedicated to guitar amplifier design and construction.

http://www.duncanamps.com - A site with many useful resources and schematics, including the "Tone Stack Calculator," a program allowing you to model common types of tone circuits. The site also includes the "tube data sheet locator" for finding tube performance data online.

http://www.el34world.com/forum/index.php - Hoffman Amplifiers Guitar Tube Amp Forum. A useful site for discussions on amplifier design and repair.

http://www.freewebs.com/valvewizard/index.html - The Valve Wizard has posted many useful papers on tube amplifier design on this site.

http://www.music-electronics-forum.com - Music Electronics Forum. Another userful site for discussions on amplifier design and repair.

http://www.webervst.com/tubes1/calcbias.htm - This site has resources and tools you can use to choose appropriate bias conditions for output stages.

http://www.nj7p.org – This site has an extensive directory of tube performance data.

Kuehnel, Richard *Guitar Amplifier Preamps* (Seattle, WA: Pentode Press, 2007).

Langford-Smith, F., Editor *Radiotron Designer's Handbook* (Harrison, NJ: Radio Corporation of America, 1960). An in-depth engineering reference.

O'Connor, Kevin *The Ultimate Tone* (London, Canada: Power Press Publishing, 1995-2008). A continuing series covering all aspects of guitar amplifier design.

Pittman, Aspen *The Tube Amp Book* (Sylmar, CA: Groove Tubes, 1993). Includes a large collection of tube guitar amplifier schematics.

*RCA Receiving Tube Manual RC-30* (Tempe, AZ: Antique Electronic Supply). Includes performance data on most tubes commonly used in guitar amplifiers, as well as design guidelines. One of a number of reprinted tube data manuals.

Rozenblit, Bruce *Beginner's Guide to Tube Audio Design* (Peterborough, NH: Audio Amateur Press, 2001).

Touzelet, Pierre "A Graphical Evaluation of Harmonic Distortion in Valves," *AudioXpress*, July 2008, p.42.

# Index

## *About the Author*

I've been involved in music and electronics since the 60's, when I electrified my ukulele. My parents had a Magnavox record player, whose ceramic cartridge plugged into the amplifier via a RCA jack. I bought a contact microphone from the local electronics store, attached it to my ax, plugged in to the Magnavox, and counted off "Memphis."

That seemed to get my parents' attention, so they bought me a Heathkit shortwave radio kit for Christmas, along with a Weller "pistol-grip" soldering iron. I assembled the radio, attached the antenna, turned it on, and it started howling. I couldn't get it to work right until I resoldered every joint in the radio.

By this time we'd moved to Jersey, and I started buying my own equipment. First up was a Lafayette amplifier, which, if I recall correctly, used two 6BQ5's in its push-pull output stage. I connected the amplifier to the 12" speaker in the console TV in my bedroom, and plugged my uke into the phono input. I had no idea why it sounded so bassy...

I upgraded to electric guitar in '67, when my folks bought me a used Fender Jazzmaster. I joined a band with my friends, but I needed an amp, so I emptied my savings account and bought an Ampeg Gemini II at the local music store. Luckily, it included the dolly, since I had to push it all the way home.

I took that rig to Cornell University, where I studied Electrical Engineering, including a couple of courses on electronic music taught by Robert Moog. I also took every music class I could, and worked part time as an electronics technician at the Cornell Synchrotron. My guitar never sounded quite right to me, so I started by changing the speaker in the amp, and then, in '70, I sold the Jazzmaster and bought a Gibson ES-335, which I still play today. The Ampeg went next, first for a Marshall Major, then a long string of other amps.

After graduation I headed out to Santa Barbara, where I worked for a couple of years testing integrated circuits for Burroughs. I was still playing in bands, and I started building my own equipment, both amps and speaker systems. I then moved to San Francisco, where I eventually ended up working at Dolby Laboratories as an audio engineer. I learned much of what you will read in Chapter 1 at Dolby.

In the last decade or so I have been taking a more orderly and comprehensive approach to amplifier design. I began, like most designers, by repairing and modifying various Fender, Ampeg, Marshall, and other designs. Later, I began constructing new amplifiers, first using existing units, such as Fender Bassmen, as platforms, and then designing and constructing all electrical and mechanical parts of the amplifier. Each amplifier was used in performances with various guitars, speakers, and effects systems.